QUALITY
UNSURPASSED

1891-1991

A CENTURY OF CALIFORNIA PORTLAND CEMENT COMPANY

Printed in the United States by
Franklin Press, San Bernardino, California.

4

The CPCC trademark is a registered (1991) service mark of
California Portland Cement Company.

Library of Congress Cataloging-in-Publication Data
Quality Unsurpassed: A Century of California Portland
Cement Company.
91-076086

QUALITY UNSURPASSED
CONTENTS

INTRODUCTION

THIS PUBLICATION CELEBRATES THE 100TH ANNIVERSARY OF THE INCORPORATION OF THE CALIFORNIA PORTLAND CEMENT COMPANY.

Corporations, by their very nature, often have a longer life span than people. It is people, however, who provide the life blood of any corporation. That has certainly been the case with *California Portland Cement*. It has been the people at all levels, working to maintain the Company's early slogan — "QUALITY UNSURPASSED," that have made the centennial possible.

Some of those people are noted in this publication. Those selected for inclusion are not necessarily people who have made the greatest contributions. They are simply people who, during the course of research on this project, became known to the author. They represent all the employees who, through the century, worked in the offices and quarries, the mills and the batch plants, the laboratories and warehouses. Those who sacked, stacked and delivered Colton, Mojave and Arizona Cement, Catalina Pacific Concrete and Colton Lime.

They are, to a large extent, people who spent a long and productive working career with "the cement plant." For to them, *California Portland Cement* was simply "the cement plant."

A remarkable number of these employees spent thirty years or more with the company. An even larger number can trace family associations with the plants well beyond the three decade mark. Fathers, uncles, grandfathers, brothers, and cousins worked for the company, sometimes extending the family tradition into the third generation.

This centennial publication concludes with a tribute to those who served forty years or more with *California Portland Cement*.

It is dedicated, however, to those who are currently employees and will be the heart — and the soul — of the corporation in the coming century.

PRODUCTION PEOPLE

PRODUCTION PEOPLE ARE THOSE MOST CLOSELY ASSOCIATED WITH MANU-
FACTURING AND DELIVERING CEMENT AND CONCRETE. They are the people who
work in the plants.

In some cases, however, the distinction between those in the plants and those
working in the corporate office may not be entirely clear. Although Wilson C. Hanna and
Ernie Hendrickson were working at the plant sites, they both obtained the position of
Vice President in the company.

California Portland produced its first cement in 1894. The company history could
begin at that point in time and proceed in straight chronological order. It does not.

Production People begins at the fiftieth anniversary of the company and looks both
back at its history and forward to what is to come. We have the decided advantage of
knowing what the second fifty years will bring.

Appraising what was accomplished in the second half of the company's centennial
may be routine as we look from the perspective of 1991, but if we step back in time to
1941 and look at what was accomplished in the last five decades, it is intriguing to note
both how much had remained the same and how much had changed.

Many people working at the cement plants and batch plants in the 1990's could boast
of long service with the company. In some cases they could look at relatives who also had
spent many years with the company. They are the personnel resources which remained
constant. Limestone was the mineral resource which remained the basis for producing
cement, but the methods and technology applied to the production process changed
tremendously between 1941 and 1991.

There is no mystery in the choice of 1941 as the platform from which to view the past
and the spring board for a look into the future. It was an easy middle point, the year
production finally matched the peak set in 1928, and a time when the company was on
the brink of expansion.

In less than a decade and a half there would be three plants in two states, two
additional cement brands being marketed, and a sharing of staff between facilities.

With almost continual modernization and expansion each of the three cement plants
found themselves in friendly competition for the title "most modern."

Modern technology did not smooth out the ups and downs of the economy to
which cement production and concrete delivery is closely tied. It also did not eliminate
the need for production people — although their titles and duties may have changed with
the times.

Chapter One

THE MOUNTAIN – MT. SLOVER
COLTON

"...was the heart of the company."

In 1941 California Portland Cement Company celebrated its fiftieth anniversary as a corporation. During those five decades the corporate headquarters in Los Angeles had moved several times, but the company letterhead usually stated "Works at Colton." Colton — or more specifically the mineral deposit know as Mt. Slover — was the heart of the company in 1941, just as it had been since California Portland was founded in 1891.

Few who helped California Portland Cement celebrate its initial 50 years could imagine that during the next five decades two additional plants would be constructed, the prestigious job of kiln burner would be one of several duties assigned to a control operator working with computers, the Colton plant would be completely remodeled without missing a day of production, and all the plants would have the capability of operating on a number of different fuel sources.

Colton Cement — that was what the bags of cement made from limestone quarried, crushed, fired and finished at the mountain named for Isaac Slover had proclaimed for half a century. Colton Cement was the major product of California Portland Cement Company.

An anniversary visitor to the "Works at Colton," could, in 1941, come into direct contact with much of the history of the company. Portions of Mill A, which had produced the first California Portland Cement in 1894, could still be easily identified. Although no longer making cement, the kiln had been adapted to lime production and was still in use.

Touring the plant, a visitor could still see the building which was identified as the old cooperage — and if he or she went inside, some of the old barrel staves would have been discovered scattered around. It had been many years since cement was shipped in barrels, but that was still a unit of measurement for selling. Four of the modern 94 pound sacks were the equivalent of a barrel. The commonly understood principle held a barrel was the chosen method of shipment because that was what two men could load on to a transport vehicle. The amount of cement in a sack was determined by the amount needed to produce a cubic foot of concrete.

Few who helped California Portland Cement celebrate its initial 50 years could imagine . . .

A covered chute and gravity fed quarry rock to the crusher at Mill A.

There were no coopers making barrels on the payroll in 1941. There were no mule tenders either, but there were people who could remember the days when these existed. Plant Superintendent Ernie Hendrickson was one.

He had hired on in the first decade of the twentieth century, charged with the responsibility of bringing water to the mules which hauled the rock from the quarry. He could still recall the quarry foreman as one of the tallest men he, as a young teenager, had ever seen. He remembered well the revolver which was customarily strapped to the foreman's waist and extended down his leg.

He remembered Mill A and the gravity feed chute which brought rock to the mill from half way up the side of the mountain. Nearly all the structures which constituted the present plant had been erected during his time — and some of them were reaching beyond the second decade of their life.

The mountain, of course, had grown considerably smaller, although it still looked fairly formidable. It was no longer the large mound-like mountain it had been in 1906 when work on Mill B was begun. Years of blasting had produced a much more angular appearance. There was a real peak pointing skyward now. Still, there was a good deal of limestone left in the mountain and business was good.

Production in 1941 would match the plant's largest output in history, which had taken place in 1928. The decade of the 1930's, which included the Great Depression, had been difficult one for all of the country.

original barrel cover

GROWTH / CHANGE

1892	Construction begins on Mill A
1894	C.P.C.C. produces first cement
1895	Mill begins 24-hr. operation
1896	Plant closes temporarily
1899	Additional land at Mt. Slover leased
1900	New Ball and grit mill added to plant
1903	Hanna begins work as Night Chemist
1904	Plant closes
1905	Plant reopens
1906	Construction begins on Mill B
1907	Mill B begins producing cement
1911	Fleming Dust Collection System installed
1914	Mill A converts to quicklime production
1917	Flying American flag on Mt. Slover begins
1927	Fleming Park donated to the city of Colton
1930's	Colton cement used in Hoover Dam
1938	First delivery in company trucks
1939	Veteran's Memorial Park given to Colton
1944	First accident free year
1945	Mill A closes
1952	Flying of flag day / night concluded
1958	1,000 successive accident-free days
1960	Modernization project begins
1963	Modernization project completed
1964	Last delivery in company trucks
1985	Cogeneration power plant completed

Men worked with machines and mules bringing limestone out of Mt. Slover in the early days of production.

Production in 1941 would match the plant's largest output in history.

L.C. Clark,
electrician Foreman,
and
"The Electric Gang."

Many companies failed during the decade and it had been hard times for the cement plant, but it continued to operate.

Work programs sponsored by the government helped provide a need for cement. Large building projects such as Hoover Dam, which included 1-1/2 million barrels of

Los Angeles City Hall - completed in 1928 using Colton cement

Colton Cement, and some of the more significant projects in the Los Angeles area helped keep production going.

Plant employees visiting Los Angeles, could look with pride at the City Hall and the Memorial Coliseum. They were among a wide variety of buildings which relied upon Colton Cement. In later years they would be able to drive on freeways with roads and bridges constructed from their cement and compare the structures of the 1920's and 1930's with those of a later period such as the Bonaventure Hotel in Los Angeles and the San Diego Convention Center, which had been constructed with Colton Cement.

Just as there had been change in the buildings using Colton Cement, there had been changes in the plant itself. Ernie Hendrickson certainly had experienced a good deal of change during his time at the plant. As Plant Superintendent he was in charge of production and had seen changes in both the physical plant and the way things were done.

By 1941 most of the workers were covered by a recently signed contract with the United Cement, Lime & Gypsum Workers' International Union, working 5 days a week, 8 hours a day.

Many workers, however, could still remember the lean years during The Depression and the more casual hiring practices of the 1920's, as well as "roll call" hiring during the decade of the 1930's.

The Plant Superintendent George Olsen or perhaps one of the shift foreman, would stand at the payroll office at the plant entrance and call the names of workers needed for the next shift.

It was a routine task and it is highly unlikely that the Superintendent would have recognized the relationship between his roll call and the patriotic exhortations of Sam Walter Foss who, in a book of poems published the year after California Portland began producing cement, issued the challenge "...bring me men to match my mountains..."

That charge was chiseled above the columns of the classic Greek style state office building erected in California's capitol in 1928 and it was exactly what the Superintendent was doing every working day — selecting men to match the mountain.

Tony Alvarez and the men who waited with him knew by sight the supervisor reading the names. It might be Olsen or Dewey Bushong or Ross Hubbs, but whoever it was — that man controlled their fate for the day. His voice projected either hope or despair for those below the platform, waiting for the roll call which took place before each of the three work shifts. .

Work was irregular at first, but as day workers learned more, became more skilled, and the supervisors came to notice and appreciate their efforts, they were told to skip the daily work call and report directly to the job site. They

The ladies were far more prominent than the dates in these calendars publicizing Oro Grande Lime and Stone.

Other marketing tools dealt more directly with the use of the product.

had become employees and no longer needed to stand outside the plant grounds waiting for an invitation to work.

There were many expectant faces during those hard years, for those who did not hear their names called at the cement plant had to look elsewhere for work or return for a later roll call - and work was hard to find.

Virgil Hamilton, who eventually became the foreman of the Lime Plant, could recall working as a meat cutter during the 1930's and having his wages cut from $25 a week to $18 every other week. Unable to make a living at that rate, he found work cutting brush in the Lytle Creek region three days a week and perched on the steps of the cement plant the remaining time until Plant Superintendent George Olsen finally tired of walking around him and suggested Hamilton replace an employee who had recently been fired. Hamilton had worked at the plant during the 1920's and had experience working at other cement plants as well.

The Lime Plant, officially Oro Grande Lime & Stone Company, shared the plant site with the cement company, but was separate from it. Oro Grande served as the marketing agent for California Portland Cement, but it also marketed lime used in the building trades and as an ingredient in everything from glass bottles to medicine and poultry feeds.

Rock was quarried for the Lime Plant and sorted by hand. Despite numerous efforts to develop some form of mechanical sorter, hand sorting remained in use until the process shut down in the 1980's.

California Portland Cement occupied the majority of the space at the site, with three mills in operation, although Mill A had been converted to lime production. Cement had been and remained the principle product of the company for nearly the entire century of its existence. There were over twice as many men working in Sacking and Loading alone at the cement plant as there were in the lime plant.

In the 1940's Sacking and Loading had more men assigned to it than any of the other sections. The quarry and grinding mills required the next largest work force, followed by Yards and Roads and the Repair Shop. Smaller numbers were assigned to the Kilns, Wet End, Dust House, Electrical Department, Machine Shop, Pipe Shop, Welding Shop, Office and Stores, Repair Shop, Carpenter Shop,

Taking rock from the quarry required a large labor force before mechanization.

Customers had been charged ten cents for each cloth sack.

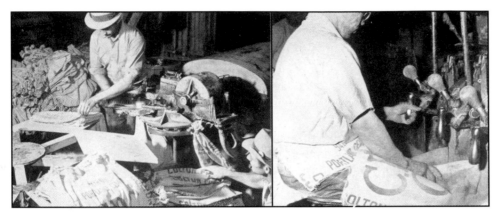 

Self closing sacks had been a feature of Colton cement for decades, but the tops still had to be tied.

Shipping Office, and Truck Repair. The union seniority list for 1941 lists three people working with the Crusher and even John "Heavy" Brokaw who later became a shovel operator, is the sole person listed under "Miscellaneous."

Sacking was done by blowing the cement into sacks which had a self-closing feature. Once they were full, the weight of the contents would serve to seal the fill opening. Cloth sacks had been used originally and the customer had been charged an additional 10 cents for each of the sacks.

The importance of the sacks could be found in the agreement to reimburse J.R. Toberman, who was serving as President of the company, in the late 1890's. He had served for three years without compensation. In January 1898, the Board of Directors voted 300 barrels of cement as compensation — but he had to return the sacks.

Sack cleaners, sorters and menders (the company employed men to mend those sacks which were returned damaged), were at the bottom of the pay scale in the 1940's. Each of the three classes earned 80 cents an hour, working a forty hour week. With the advent of the lined paper sack, the buzz of the sewing machines was no longer a part of the cement plant scene, but the equipment remained for many years, surprising those who entered the building and for whom cloth sacks were known only in tales told by "old timers."

Moisture was a major concern in the shipment of cement. The product needed to arrive at the customer as a powder — not a solid block. At one point the company used a sack which had a color code. If the CPC initials turned red the contents had been exposed to moisture and were not to be used in high pressure oil well applications.

Liners were added to the paper sacks to prevent the encroachment of moisture, One of the tasks of those working in the chemical laboratory was to determine whether or not the sacks were moisture proof. Sacks filled with cement were placed in the "Fog Room" and subjected to various amounts of mist and

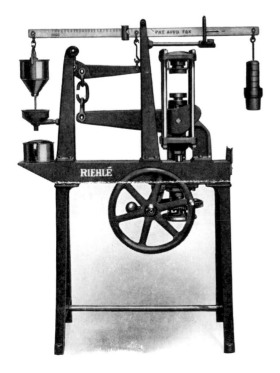

Community programs often used Colton Cement themes

Working for the cement plant was often a family affair.

Wilson C. Hanna began working as the night chemist in the laboratory in 1903.

moisture. They would then be removed and the cement tested. The company did not make its own bags, but it wanted to be very sure that those they used met company specifications.

Product and quality testing were the responsibility of the laboratory. Wilson C. Hanna was in charge of the laboratory. He was also unofficially in charge of the lime operation. It was rumored around the plant that if you wanted a new pencil for the lime operation, you would have to show Mr. Hanna the used stubs of the old ones before receiving replacements.

Hanna was Chief Chemist for California Portland Cement and had held that position since 1904 when Dr. Neu, who had been his teacher, left to take a position in New York.

Working in the chemical laboratory with Mr. Hanna were twelve of the 282 workers covered by the union agreement. Roscoe Schott, who became Head Physical Tester, was second on the seniority list, having started in 1924. Ralph Hubbs had begun a decade later. He was one of seven Hubbs brothers to work at the plant. Six of their sons represented the second generation of the family working for California Portland Cement.

It was not unusual for the work force to have brothers, sons, uncles and cousins included on the roster. Working for the cement plant was often very much a family affair.

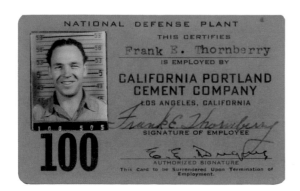
W. H.

Admit One ·· **PICNIC**
By the Employees of
The Calif. Portland Cement Co.
Orange Show Bldg.
August 11, 1934
Dinner Drinks Peanuts Candy Popcorn Ice Cream

COMPLIMENTS OF

Members of the Campa family can count three direct generations, as well as many other relatives, among the Campa, Chavez, Cimental, Corral, Guerrero and Castorena families, including Arturo Castorena who retired in 1969 after being originally hired in 1920.

These strong family ties led to a rich history of "cement plant stories" which could be repeated at family gatherings. Some may even have originated at functions such as the 1934 company picnic which, according to newspaper accounts, brought together "some 1600 persons" at the National Orange Show grounds on an August evening.

Executives from the Los Angeles office joined with plant employees and their families to enjoy good food and entertainment which included the company band, directed by William Atkinson. The newspaper noted, "The expense of the entire picnic was borne by the company..."

History was not something foreign to the men working at the cement plant. Despite the numbers which appeared at the picnic, the plant crew was relatively small when separated into individual departments and three working shifts every day. People usually got to know their fellow workers.

There was often plenty of time to know one another well, as lengthy terms of employment were common. Frank Thornberry had forty-five years of service when he retired– and the company had only been in existence for 90 years. Basilio Martinez had reached the fifty year mark before he retired.

Those who had been around for some years — and it

Chemist was the key . . . to success or failure.

was common to work for the plant for a number of years — could tell stories of the origin of the equipment as well as the early days of the company.

It was rumored that the large steam shovel slowly moving along its railbed in the quarry had worked on the Panama Canal project before coming to Colton. The shovel ate away at the rock blasted from the face of the quarry until a site was clear and additional rail had to be laid before moving on.

Wilson C. Hanna, who signed his correspondence with the corporate office simply, "Chemist," had begun working at Colton in 1903 . As Chief Chemist it was his responsibility to make sure all the ingredients which were needed to produce cement went together in just the right proportions.

The chemists were set apart from most of the others who worked in the plant. The vast majority of the other workers seldom, if ever, entered the laboratory.

It was understood that the laboratory staff preferred to work in something akin to "splendid isolation." They were, even at this time, the very heart of the cement making process. They determined the correct mixture of ingredients and checked to be sure the product was of the correct consistency.

When the company had first been established, it was the chemist — and he alone — who was the key to success or failure. The founders had recognized this fact and obtained exclusive use of the cement making process patented by George Duryee.

If you lost your chemist, you would be hard pressed to continue to operate. Most of the plant staff knew this — and so did the chemist.

Mr. Hanna was something of an institution. He could tell you a good deal about how the plant operated and what had happened during the first half century.

The Directors recognized his importance to the company's history and, in the early 1930's, asked him to provide a record of his experiences. Mr. Hanna responded with a several page memo recounting his experiences over the previous three decades.

Thirty years was a pretty good career, but Mr. Hanna spent over two additional decades with the company, making him the longest term employee in California Portland Cement's history.

He knew from personal experience that it not been easy going for the plant in the early years of the 20th Century. By 1902 there were over 100 employees at the plant and by February of the following year the

TIME BOOK for the																		
NAMES	1	2	3	4	5	6	7	8	9	10	11	12	13	14	15	16	17	18
James Pregean				8	8	8		8	8									
L.E. Pake	7		4	9	9	10	9	9		9		9	4					
J. Crackery			12	12	12	9	9											
Chas Burley	12	12	12	12	12	12	12	12	12	12	12	12	12	12	12	12	12	12
a. Higgs	11	12	12	12	12	12	10	12	12	9	9							9
Jim Adkins			9	9	9	9	9											
J.K. Bailest			8	8	8	10	8	7										
J.L. Merkley		9	10	9	10	9	9		9	9	9	9	9		9	9		

value of the company property was estimated at $1,000,000, with the cement plant alone worth $350,000.

At one point in 1904, however, the plant had been closed and was reduced to two permanent employees, Hanna and the Night Watchman, Charley Burley. While Hanna was just beginning with the company, Burley had been with it for several years working 12 hour shifts, seven days a week and seldom missing a day, although at one point he did cut back to an 8 hour day to celebrate Christmas.

The plant rebounded from this low point and was soon strong enough to support an expansion. Work on the construction of Mill B, located on the South side of Mt. Slover, was begun in 1906 and the first commercial portland cement from the new plant was produced on November 5th of the following year. The Mill B Plant had five times the capacity of Mill A.

Expansion continued with the construction of Mill C during 1912 — 1914. The newest addition was capable of producing 2,500 barrels of cement daily.

Changes did not always take the form of entire new mills. Visitors to Colton could identify structures and buildings which had been added on an individual basis through the years.

One of the most important was the dust collection building. Occupying a space 75 feet by 125 feet, this structure housed a dust

UNITED STATES PATENT OFFICE.

GEORGE DURYEE, OF ORANGE, NEW JERSEY.

PROCESS OF MANUFACTURING CEMENT.

SPECIFICATION forming part of Letters Patent No. 417,634, dated December 17, 1889.

Application filed March 30, 1889. Serial No. 305,407. (No specimens.)

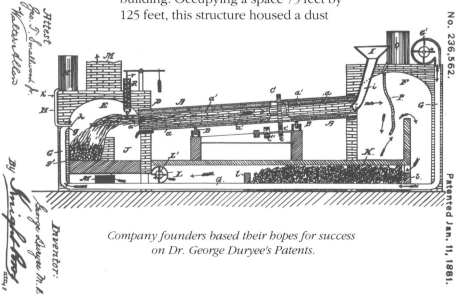

No. 236,562.

G. DURYEE.
Metallurgic Furnace.

Patented Jan. 11, 1881.

Company founders based their hopes for success on Dr. George Duryee's Patents.

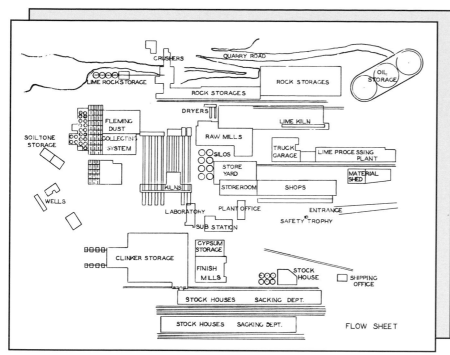

After 1911 all kilns were connected to the Fleming Dust Collection System

Fleming made frequent trips to Colton.

collection system developed by Thomas J. Fleming, who had served for many years as Secretary and General Manager of the company. It was initially used on September 10, 1911 and recaptured 90% of the cement dust escaping from the kilns. This not only contributed to a cleaner environment, but was also more efficient, as the recovered dust was a marketable product.

Mr. Hanna, who readily admitted that his father's acquaintance with some of the members of the Board of Directors could have been a factor in his being hired at the plant, knew General Manager Fleming. Although a part of the corporate staff in Los Angeles, Fleming made frequent trips to Colton. He had undertaken a comprehensive

inspection of the plant shortly after being named General Manager.

Fleming was not a chemist. His contributions had been as the inventor of the Fleming Dust Collector System and as a policy maker. Hanna's work was at the site and very much involved with the day to day activities.

One of the very few staff members to actually hold stock in the company, Hanna regularly gave his voting proxy to Mr. Fleming and, after Fleming's death, to Mr. Duque, the company president. Hanna focused on making cement at the plant.

That task became much more difficult after December 7, 1941, when the United States became an active participant in World War II.

During the early part of 1941 it was relatively easy for people in the U.S. to consider the war in Europe as something which took place "over there."

It was still possible to vividly recall World War I. Perhaps the most notable reminder of both that conflict and the feeling of American patriotism was the United States flag which flew 24 hours a day high atop Mt. Slover.

It had first been raised in 1917 after Thomas Fleming had received special permission from Congress to fly it both day and night. In 1941 it had been joined by a the California state flag and moved to another location on the mountain.

Mill B was the first plant on the south side of the mountain.

Plant Chemnist, Edward Duryee, second from left, looks a bit over dressed in this turn of the century staff photo.

". . . Colton's Liberty Flag is a Wondrous Spectacle. "

The time the first 30 foot by 20 foot flag was raised, Mt. Slover was one of only three places in the country granted the right to fly the flag at night. It required, of course, that the flag be illuminated after dark. On July 5, 1917 the front page of the San Bernardino Daily Sun proclaimed "PARIS CHEERS PERSHING'S TROOPS" and "UNFURLING OF COLTON'S LIBERTY FLAG IS A WONDROUS SPECTACLE." Some could recall, if they remembered their days in American History at nearby Colton High School, that 1917 marked the year America had joined the Allies in World War I.

In 1941, none could know that it would be just a matter of months before the illumination of the flag would jeopardize the security of a nation at war and the 24 hour tradition would have to be suspended. It would be reinstated after the war and remain in place until the mountain had diminished to such a degree that it was no longer feasible to fly the flag.

While wars and preparation for war often meant new construction and an increased need for cement, it also meant there would be far fewer men available to work in the plant.

During the war years just keeping enough men on the payroll to maintain production became a major struggle. It was not uncommon for men to work two full shifts — quite a change from the Depression years when shifts had been cut to fewer hours to provide much-needed employment for more workers.

1944 – recorded a full year without a lost time accident and was awarded First Safety Award

Despite the strain of long hours and the normal hazards associated with quarry work, transportation of the rock down the hill, working around crushers, rotating kilns, mills, and large pieces of equipment, California Portland Cement achieved one of its most notable successes during the war years. In 1944, with production at 4,350,000 barrels, it recorded a full year without a lost time accident and was awarded the Portland Cement Association's Safety Award in recognition of the accomplishment.

The concrete monument used Colton cement and was firmly embedded at the entrance to the parking area on August 21, 1945. It has been relocated from its initial site to its present site immediately in front of the main office building.

Joe Ivy and Plant Superintendant Ernie Hendrickson help promote Colton's first Saftey Award.

Colton's safety record continued to improve. The plant won the award three times in the late 1950's, reaching the 1000 day accident free mark in 1958 and repeating this feat in 1966. Additional annual awards were earned in 1960 and 1962.

The 1966 mark was noted by the company with the presentation of a $25.00 United States savings bond to each of the employees and a special safety rally at which Nicasio Salazar won a compact car and savings bonds worth $1,350 were awarded to employees in recognition of a job done well and safely.

California Portland Cement Company was proud of its Colton plant. In remarks prepared for the 1949 visit of the Portland Cement Association's Technical

This was the state of the art in cement production.

Committee, the company pointed with pride to the quarry described as being "over 3/4 mile long" and the Superior Jaw Crusher, 66 inches x 84 inches, which was later sent to the Mojave plant..

The remarks noted satisfaction with the Fleming Dust Collection System which had been in operation for nearly forty years and pointed to the "excellent character of adjacent orange groves" as testimony to the efficiency of the system.

Attention was called to the Finish Grinding Department which was described as one of the simplest and most highly efficient units in the industry. The laboratories were also highlighted. They were "completely equipped to carry out control, and research work." The company's progressive policy in sponsoring cooperative work with groups such as the Portland Cement Association, colleges, and the various state and federal agencies was also noted.

The Colton plant visited by the Technical Committee in 1950, however, was very different from the one inspected by a trainload of visitors 14 years later. By 1963 a com-

pletely new and modernized plant had been constructed at Colton — and it had been built around the existing plant without missing any production time. It took two years to complete the project at an approximate cost of $23,500,000.

Nine existing kilns, which had ranged from 150 feet to 205 feet in length, were replaced with two new kilns 490 feet long and 13 to 15 feet in diameter. The kilns now faced East and West, rather than North and South. They were operated from the central control room, using the most modern computers available.

The most notable feature of the computer operation was that it was supervisory in nature, not just a monitoring device. John Romig, who had become Chief Chemist and Chemical Engineer in 1958, developed on-site software for the computers which, with minor adjustments, remained in use for many years.

It was quite a change from the early days of production when the company had purchased the rights to the George Duryee patents to the modernization of the early

Computers supervised the production process, but Trailing Head Locators helped the programers know when to introduce new information.

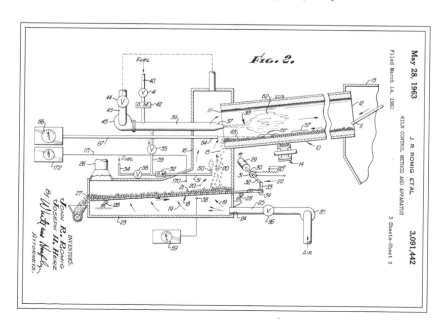

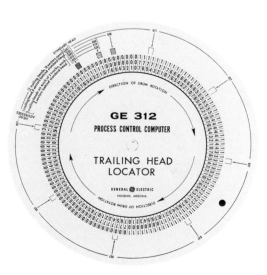

John Romig's inventions contributed to plant modernization.

Building a new plant while operating an old one was something of a novel concept...

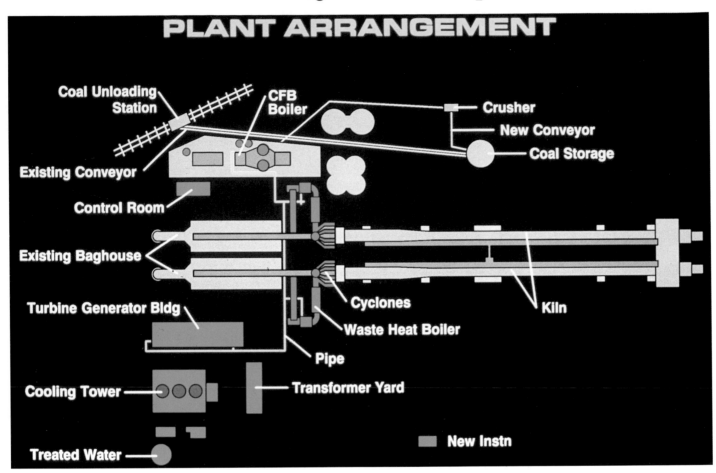

PLANT ARRANGEMENT

Coal Unloading Station

CFB Boiler

Crusher

New Conveyor

Coal Storage

Existing Conveyor

Control Room

Existing Baghouse

Turbine Generator Bldg

Cyclones

Kiln

Waste Heat Boiler

Pipe

Cooling Tower

Transformer Yard

New Instn

Treated Water

Company owned trucks made last delivery...

1960's when John Romig and Joe Herz, working for California Portland Cement, submitted applications for and were granted patents of their own.

Romig was responsible for more than just physical change in the modernization process. His interest was in the application of theory, as well as its development, and he worked directly with the production staff to provide programs and processes which had meaning and application.

Technology had challenged the chemists' "splendid isolation." But, John Romig personally set the stage for more direct interaction between the laboratory people and those in production.

Colton was installing equipment designed to provide state-of-the-art cement production and it tended to be a bit awe inspiring. R.G. "Pat" Patterson, who headed the company's engineering department, could often be found at the Colton plant during the modernization. He was watching the installation of the control panels when he proclaimed the company needed an instruction manual for every gauge and switch on every panel in the room.

The assignment was handed to a recently hired young engineer in his twenties named Ron Evans, who just happened to be standing nearby in the control room, having taken a brief leave from his normal assignment

Company cement carriers changed significantly in the nearly three decades they were used

. . . the project was complete by March 1963.

Artist's rendering of Colton energy cogeneration plant.

"Electrical energy self-sufficiency"

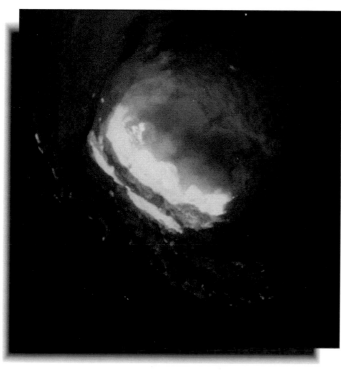

*Temperatures in the kiln burning zone
may reach 3000 degrees Fahrenheit*

inspecting the pourings for a new building foundation nearby. In this case curiosity did not kill the cat, but it certainly provided him with a monumental responsibility.

Training staff as control room operators proved an interesting task. Throughout its entire history, the company, had employed kiln burners. These were people whose knowledge of how to keep a kiln burning at just the right temperature was admired throughout the plant. Often this was a matter of visually checking the flame in the kiln to determine if it "looked right" and then making the necessary corrections. It was something of an art.

With the completion of the modernization, a control operator had responsibility for the entire production process from raw mix to cement storage and each step in the process was controlled from the central control room, not at the mix or kiln location. Experienced kiln burners often found it difficult to wean themselves from the visual inspection of the kilns and become accustomed to reading dials and "remote" controls.

Building a new plant while operating an old one was something of a novel concept and an even more monumental task. It was quite different than just adding to an existing operation. The task was complicated by the fact that the old facility had been on the site for more than 50 years. This meant that there was an excellent possibility that the water and electrical lines did not go exactly as the

Major concerns ... cost of fuel and environmental issues.

*Colton's 490 foot kilns were an
integal part of the modernization.*

drawings indicated, having been modified many times during the course of the years.

Naturally, the chances for interrupting electrical or water service at any given time during the excavations for new structures were very good. Once this happened there was a good deal of scurrying around to make the repairs as quickly as possible and restore full service to the plant. After a short time, the engineering and construction people became quite proficient at these repairs.

By March of 1963 the project was complete and the California Portland Cement Company proclaimed this the most modern cement plant in the country. It had an annual capacity of 750,000 tons and a production staff of 248. Production capacity was no longer expressed in barrels, which, of course, had not been used for many decades, but in the more meaningful unit of "tons." For easy conversion a ton of cement was approximately 5.3 barrels.

1963 was also the year which marked the beginning of the end for cement delivery in company owned trucks. The final delivery was made in January of 1964. After nearly a quarter of a century, California Portland Cement returned to the use of contract truckers. The transition was not as easy as it appeared on the surface. The company fleet could not simply be dumped on the market, if contracts with existing carriers were to be honored. The equipment had to be decommissioned carefully.

The last half of the 1970's brought violence and tragedy to a facility which thought itself separate from such activity. A series of fires both at the plant and at the homes of plant personnel was determined to be the work of an arsonist. In

one instance a supervisor was fired upon while investigating a fire. Another supervisor was injured by a shotgun blast while at his home.

The most tragic event, however, was the murder of Chuck Osberg, Colton Plant Manager. He was killed while sitting at a counter in his den on Christmas Eve, 1980. The death remains an unsolved mystery.

Although the murder was not related to company activities, for a relatively small and close knit work force at the plant, it had a very significant impact. Accidents and fatalities had been experienced at the plant before. Lives had been lost in a quarry blast in 1948. The first industrial accident which resulted in a death was recorded in the summer of 1900 when an employee of a painting contractor working at the plant accidently touched an electrical wire.

There was, however, a significant difference between an accident and murder. The violence stopped with the death of Chuck Osberg, but supervisory and management employees were provided with additional security for a considerable time after his death.

A community of workers accustomed to the physical shocks of quarry blasting had to adjust to the personal shock of assassination. It was a difficult time for the staff, but one through which they passed.

The work continued. Even in the most modern of plants there was always room for improvement. Two major concerns confronted the plant management in the next two decades after modernization. One was the cost of fuel and the other was an increased emphasis on environmental issues.

Nearly anything which would burn could be used to fuel a kiln. The early bottle kilns on Mt. Slover had used wood. California Portland's initial kilns had burned fuel oil. At a later date natural gas had been used only to be replaced by coal in the 1970s. There are different burn qualities to these latter three fuels, but all could be used. Two of the major factors in determining which was used were availability and price.

Regardless of which fuel was used, burning the kiln produced a great deal of heat, much of which was lost. This was not energy efficient and energy was not cheap. The 1981 annual report noted a "rapidly escalating cost of electrical power," which contributed significantly to the cost of producing a ton of cement.

By 1981 engineering studies for the feasibility of an electrical cogeneration facility at Colton had been completed. This was designed to capture and utilize some of the heat escaping from the kilns. The company obtained the permits necessary to begin construction and ground was broken in December 1982. A completion date in mid-1985 was projected for the $40 million project, which would result in "electrical energy self-sufficiency."

Heat, however, was not the only thing lost into the air

*Photo illustrates overflow
Ball Mill for wet grinding*

in the cement making process. Complaints about "cement dust" in the Colton area could be traced back to the early years of the Twentieth Century. In response to the complaints, the company had developed the Fleming Dust Collection System and put it into use in 1911.

Although the system had been modified through the years, it had functioned for four decades. A more modern and effective system had been included in the 1963 plant modernization. This "bag house" filtration system forced the emissions through over 4,000 inflated fiberglass bags, which captured the dust while letting the air pass through. Each of the kilns was connected to a bag house. Nearly two decades later two additional bag houses were constructed for the cooler area.

In a world increasingly concerned with protecting the environment, California Portland Cement continued to work to meet standards developed by environmental protection and regulation agencies. With the passage of time, standards became more stringent and the company responded accordingly, as it had throughout its history.

Employees such as Jan Stevens, Gene Juarez, Louis Moten, and Dave Shepherd, working at Colton in the last quarter of the Twentieth Century, are reminded of that history daily as they pass the Portland Cement Association Safety Award, now relocated to a position of prominence immediately adjacent to the main office building's front entrance.

They know Mill A, Wilson C. Hanna, Ernie Hendrickson, and George Olsen through old photos hung in the halls of the laboratory building and in company histories.

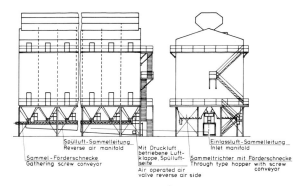

Glass Bag House – typical side and end elevation

It was not difficult for them to recall the completion of the cogeneration power facility or the construction of the new finish mills. The finish grinding mill project, budgeted for $16 million in 1979, was a relatively new improvement. It replaced eight grinding mills which dated to the 1920's with two new mills. The replacement allowed Colton to more efficiently produce greater quantities of speciality cements. Both this project and the cogeneration plant were completed in the early 1980's.

To the employees of the 1980's and 1990's these were simply projects which modernized and improved the plant. They were not history. In reality, of course, whenever a bit of the past is removed — as in the case of the old grinding mills — or something is added to the present, history is created for the future.

When we remove a bit of the past – we create history for the future.

ARIZONA — THE BEGINNING
RILLITO

"...part of the marketing area..."

Fred Kennett came to work at the Colton plant in 1948. He didn't stay long. Fred was an engineer and a draftsman. One of his first jobs was designing the mill building for a new plant in Arizona. He would spend a good portion of his over three decade career with California Portland Cement watching the plant just outside Tucson grow and develop.

While the name of the company was California Portland, Arizona had been considered part of the marketing area from the beginning. The agreements signed with George Duryee for the use of his patents had defined a market area which included the Territory of Arizona.

In 1895 the company had entered into a contract with the Agua Fria Construction Company of Phoenix. California Portland would provide all the cement needed by the construction company and only Colton cement would be used in the construction projects, both current and future. In addition Agua Fria would be the agent for Colton cement in selling to the building trade in Arizona.

Interest continued after the turn of the century. Minutes of the July 16, 1901 Board of Director's meeting stated, "Mr. Jackson's reports from Arizona were read and approved." The market for cement, however, must have been quite competitive.

Four years later the University of Arizona Engineering Department, published Bulletin No. 1 which reported on

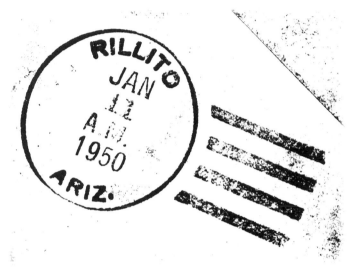

In 1895 the company entered into a contract agreement with Agua Fria Construction.

Exploration for an appropriate site... took place during the 1920's and 1930's.

the testing of seven domestic cements and four foreign brands. Colton was one of two domestics from California. The others were from Arizona, Colorado, Kansas, Pennsylvania and New Jersey. The foreign brands were from Germany, England and Belgium.

While not listing test results for each of the brands, the bulletin concluded that domestic cement in general evidenced a "decided superiority." Despite this fact, the bulletin made it clear that there was a seeming preference for the foreign product, even at a significantly higher price. A German brand was used "almost exclusively" in the Tucson market and in the Phoenix area over $15,000 — a substantial amount of money in 1905 — had been expended for imported cement.

Whatever efforts Agua Fria Construction had made in selling Colton cement ten years earlier, they clearly had not garnered and maintained a significant share of the market.

Although the university tested a cement supposedly made in Arizona, the Engineering Department concluded there was a need for a cement factory to be operated successfully in Arizona so the local market could have the product at a moderate price. California Portland, though hardly in a position to develop a new plant in the early 1900's, had reached the same conclusion.

Exploration for appropriate sites and feasibility studies for a plant in Arizona took place during the

1920's and 1930's. Difficult economic times prevented any new venture during the Depression years and the first half of the 1940's was consumed with the war effort.

It was not until the post-war boom that the company was ready to move into Arizona with a complete plant. In

GROWTH / CHANGE	
1895	Contract with Agua Fria Construction of Phoenix approved for use and marketing of Colton cement
1920's	Exploration for Arizona plant site
1947	Marketing and manufacturing surveys completed
1948	Board approves $3,000,000 expenditure for construction
	Donald R. Warren Co. begins construction
1949	Arizona Portland produces first cement
1952	Plant expansion completed raising capacity to 1,500,000 barrels annually
1955	Additional kilns installed raising annual capacity to 2,700,000 barrels
1956	Plant celebrates first year without a lost time accident
1958	New grinding mill and cement storage silos completed
1960	Original powerhouse sold to local utility company
1966	Plant celebrates 1000 days without lost time injury
1973	No. 4 kiln installed, utilizing preheater
	Central computer room installed
	Conveyor belt connects quarry with main plant

Rillito kilns await increased capacity in 1955 expansion project.

Kiln Burners Clair Hawn and Joe Warner take a break with Jack Cole during Rillito expansion project.

... the University concluded there was a need
for a cement factory...

April 1948 the Board of Directors approved an expenditure of approximately $3,000,000 for the new plant. Not everyone on the Board approved of the venture, but Mr. Duque, the company President, was adamant. This was a project which would be completed.

Studies of cement manufacturing and marketing in Arizona had been conducted in 1947. They were sufficiently encouraging to justify drawing up construction contracts. The Donald R. Warren Engineering Company began work on the Rillito, Arizona facility in the Spring of 1948.

Fred Kennett soon found himself,

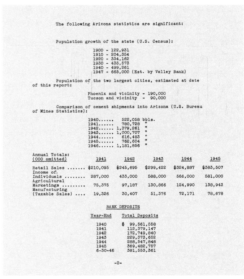

Arizona Study – 1947

along with some others from the Colton plant including R.G. "Pat" Patterson, working in cooperation with the engineering firm to transform a cotton field eighteen miles from Tucson into a cement plant.

Pat Patterson headed the engineering department for California Portland and, along with his ever present pipe, was a familiar sight whenever the company was involved with expansion or modernization projects. He had his work cut out for him in Rillito.

This was an undeveloped site in nearly every sense of the term. Even the quarry would be nearly five miles to the south. One of the first concerns was for

Construction at the Rillito site moved rapidly.

Large pieces of equipment had to be trucked in.

sufficient electricity to run the plant. This led to the development of a powerhouse which protected a huge diesel generator. The power source was so important the company provided housing for the powerhouse superintendent, Jim Nash — and that housing was placed very conveniently near the powerhouse itself. An old schoolhouse was pressed into use as the office building and chemical laboratory. O.L. McCain, the plant chemist, shared the school house with John Luten, Clair Hawn, and Lon Falassi.

During the early phases of construction, there was no railroad spur to the plant site. Large pieces of equipment had to be trucked in, providing the residents of Tucson an interesting view of the

developments taking place a few miles down the road. Sections of the first kiln slowly made their way through the town's business section aboard flatbed trucks. It was not a new kiln, but would serve the purpose, once the Allis-Chalmers people had lengthened it a bit.

The unique feature of the kiln was the fact that the sections were riveted together. Workers at the plant could, in later years, vividly recall the red hot rivets being thrown from the forge to the men pounding them into place.

By December 1949 Arizona

*Top-Power Superintendent, Jim Nash's housing.
Bottom-A.P.C.'s first kiln was delivered by truck.*

*Original mill building supports reach upward
during construction.*

The unique feature of the kiln . . .

Workmen joined sections of the original A-C kiln.

Portland Cement was producing cement.

Harry Goddard had worked on the construction of the plant and remained on as an Arizona Portland employee,

working in the grinding department. He shared with the other early staff, the experience of watching an old chain drive truck work its way to and from the quarry. Quarry Superintendent Walter Stoops and the crew who worked with him, including Orville Shield, Steve Trinidad and Albert Celeya knew the truck well.

Transportation was more of a challenge for welders such as O.E. "Mutts" Borchers. The welders had to compete with Plant Superintendent George Moyle for use of his station wagon when they needed to move the welding equipment around the plant site.

With a strong market, expansion plans began almost immediately. A $3,000,000 expansion was completed by Jan. 1952. This raised the annual capacity to 1,500,000 barrels.

The cement bags with the green cactus on the front were becoming a familiar sight in Arizona. Just to keep the symbol clearly associated with the facility, two large Saguaro Cacti were transplanted - and tenderly cared for - near the entrance to the plant in the 1970's. A growing market in Arizona during the late fifties and early sixties was reflected in improvements and additions to the Rillito site. By December 1955 capacity had risen to 2,700,000 barrels annually. A 1958 efficiency study resulted in an additional grinding mill, cement storage silos and a change in the

Thirty inches wide and nearly five miles long, the covered conveyor belt brings crushed rock from the quarry to the plant.

By 1966 Arizona Portland could boast of a capacity of 3,000,000 barrels per year.

electrical system. In addition, a transfer plant for bulk cement and a warehouse for storing sacked cement were built in Phoenix.

During 1960 the powerhouse was sold to the local utility company with the understanding that it would be maintained for backup power. The daily routine power needs would be met by the local company. By 1966 Arizona Cement could boast of three 335 foot long kilns, a capacity of 3,000,000 barrels per year, and a cotton crop

which continued to grow on the portion of the 200 acre site not occupied by the plant itself.

It could also point to a solid record of no lost time accidents, beginning in 1956. In 1966, after several

Frank Thornberry, Plant Manager, stressed safety at the "Rillito 500."

accident free years, it reached the 1000 day mark for no lost time accidents.

A thorough modernization of the plant took place in the early 1970's. A fourth kiln was placed in operation. This kiln had a preheater and a capacity to equal the existing three kilns. Originally it had been thought the new kiln would allow the older equipment to be phased out. In reality the three older kilns were only shut down for a brief period of time before rejoining the operation.

A central computer control room was established, and the long truck journey from the quarry was replaced by a covered conveyor belt which brought the rock from a crusher at the quarry to the main plant. This long arm stretching across the arid landscape became an unofficial trademark of the Rillito plant.

Access to reliable transportation had played a part in the location of the plant. It was accessible by highway, but was approximately five miles from the quarry. The unpredictable nature of the nearby Santa Cruz River had played an important part in the site selection. There was concern — which later proved justified — that a facility closer to the quarry could be isolated by flash flooding.

Although located in an adjacent state, the plant personnel were in close contact with corporate headquarters. During the early years of operation Mr. Duque had been a frequent visitor and Mr. Grant continued that tradition when he became President. There were monthly visits from Walt Koenig and staff from the accounting department often came to the facility.

The cement sacks might read Arizona Portland, to reflect the market in which the product was sold, but the plant was clearly part of California Portland Cement Co.

Preheaters and precalciners are common on modern kilns such as this addition to the A.P.C. plant.

HIGH DESERT PRODUCTION
MOJAVE

"... to meet market demands."

During 1955 Bill Mabery was looking for a few good men and women. They should know how to make cement and be willing to relocate to a rather dry climate where high winds were common. Bill had been given the responsibility for hiring the crews for California Portland Cement's new plant in the high desert near Mojave, California.

Studies commissioned by the Board of Directors in the early 1950's indicated the need for additional production in the California Portland marketing area. Although the Colton plant had been scheduled for modernization and some work on that effort had begun, it was determined that the company needed an entire new plant to meet the market demands.

In 1953 the company purchased extensive undeveloped limestone reserves near Mojave from Pacific Portland Cement Company and the following year an authorization of over $12,500,000 to build the new plant was passed by the Board.

Development of the site required the construction of nine miles of branch railroad track. Stops along rail lines or spurs usually have some name identification. This one was designated Creal in honor of Wilson Creal Hanna, the company's chief chemist for many years.

There was something of a company tradition in the naming of such stops. Much earlier in its history there had been a stop at a company owned-clay deposit which had been named Fleming for the company Secretary and General Manager.

On January 27, 1955 company dignitaries rode the locomotive of the first "train" to use the Southern Pacific branch line. It was both symbolic and useful, as the train consisted of the company men, the locomotive, a caboose, and a car loaded with Colton cement.

Portland pozzolana cement from the Colton plant had been designated for use in the construction of the new Mojave facility. L.E. Dixon Company of Los Angeles was the successful bidder on the construction project. Work was to begin on December 1st and be completed within 250 days.

The plant was expected to produce approximately two million barrels of cement annually.

Cement was not the only existing resource transported to Mojave to build and operate the new facility. Personnel from other plants and from the engineering office were also on the site during construction. R.G "Pat" Patterson was seen frequently as he headed yet another engineering project for California Portland Cement. Fred Kennett was brought in from the Rillito plant to help with the construction phase.

Beginnings of construction. . .

President E.E.Duque opens the rail line to Creal.

Mojave construction makes its mark on the desert landscape.

Fred Kennett and Pat Patterson worked as a team.

Pat and Fred were on loan for the construction and start up period. Others such as Dale Hendrickson, Jim Bruce and Gordon Anderson were transferring to the plant. They joined Assistant Superintendent Lawrence Veo, Robert Conner, O.L. McCain, Lon Falassi and Glen Hamilton working in the new plant as mill foremen, storekeepers, chemists, drillers, and laborers.

Mojave was Pat Patterson's last project for C.P.C.

Plans for modernization of the Colton plant had been in the works for some years. Dale and perhaps some of the other Colton staff rightly anticipated the modernization might mean a reduction in staff. Those who were not high on the senority list would do well to take advantage of the opportunity at Mojave. Dale, who started with the company as a laborer, has spent over four decades with California Portland, rising to Plant Superintendent at Mojave.

George Moyle transferred from the Rillito plant and was the first superintendent at Mojave. He spent nearly 6 years at the site before retiring. During his

GROWTH / CHANGE

1952	Property purchased for Mojave Plant
1954	L.E. Dixon Co. awarded construction contract
	Oak Creek Canyon property purchased
1955	So. Pacific branch line to Creal opens
	Start up of Kiln No. 1 & 2
1956	First bulk shipment of cement
1957	Start up of Kiln No. 3 & 4
1958	Start up of Kiln No. 5
1963	Kiln production reaches 1,099,172 tons
	Plant marks one year without loss time accident
1969	New bulk loading facility constructed
1970	2.000 H.P. finish mill constructed
1978	Mojave Modernization Project (MOMOD) begins
1981	First clinker produced by Kiln No. 6

Wheeled loaders at Mojave fill the fifty-ton trucks for their trip to the crusher.

CPC employees gather during construction of Mojave plant.

Mojave was going to be the most modern plant in the company.

tenure he watched over nearly constant construction and expansion at the plant. Those who followed him as superintendent and later as Plant Manager, John Lewton, Art Powell, Herman Alford, Bob Lamp and Rick Patton, could all claim a similar experience. The plant seemed to be continually changing.

January 23, 1956 marked the first bulk shipment of Mojave Cement. Six months later the first of several plant expansions was begun. Start up on kiln three and four

came in the Fall of 1957, with a fifth kiln added in the Spring of the following year. All the kilns fired under the watchful eye of Burner Foreman Clair Hawn.

Additional property had to be purchased in Oak Creek Canyon to guarantee sufficient water for a five kiln operation. This was done in 1952.

Record production from the five kilns was achieved in 1963. The total production was set at 1,099,172 tons and operation was rated at 98.9% reliability. Employee reliability was high that year also as the plant could claim a full year without any lost time injuries.

The construction of a new bulk loading facility and, in 1970, a new 2000 H.P. finish mill marked the conclusion of the plant's first fifteen years of operation. There were plans for even more improvement.

Mojave Kiln Dept. receives plant safety award 1976 from President Morphy.

Always striving to operate the most modern plants, California Portland Cement initiated MOMOD in 1978. MOMOD - Mojave Modernization Project - somehow lost the "P" for project, but everyone knew what the letters represented. Mojave was going to be the most modern plant in the company.

This $112 million project nearly doubled the amount of cement produced at Mojave, raising the total to 2.1 million tons. It was proudly described in the 1980 Annual Report as "one of the most sensible and successful projects in the history of the Company." It was also the last project on which Pat Patterson worked. His contribution to

Mojave's distinctive geodesic dome adds a contemporary touch to the desert landscape

CALIFORNIA PORTLAND CEMENT COMPANY

P.O. BOX 910, MOJAVE, CALIFORNIA 93502 / TEL. (805) 824-2401 FAX (805) 824-4908

Mojave and to California Portland is noted on a plaque mounted in the central control room.

Mojave became one of the more recognizable plants in the system with its distinctive geodesic dome storage facility. The dome was a shape particularly well suited to the desert environment, as it tended to counter the effect of the strong desert winds while protecting the crushed rock and limestone beneath its 100 foot high center.

A second distinctive feature was added to the plant skyline with the completion of the preheater flash calcining tower on kiln 6. A part of the MOMOD project, the kiln produced its first clinker in 1981. It was so successful the company later suggested perhaps the addition of two kilns rather than one would have been a good idea.

Getting the correct mixture to the kilns involved a fairly straight line process at Mojave. The flow of material within the plant was not complex. Getting the rock to the plant, however, wasn't quite so simple.

A new quarry two miles away and 825 feet above the dump for the primary crusher had to be developed. This extended the life of the reserves and provide quality limestone for the expansion. Off road dump trucks, each with a 50 ton capacity, hauled an average of 20 loads a day between the quarry and the crusher. Engineering and constructing roadways to safely accommodate the trucks took some thought and some imagination.

John Rains, worked with Steve Regis and Dave Armstrong, the quarry superintendent, to design a dirt road 60 feet wide with rock berms five to six feet high on either side and a 7% to 10% incline. At various intervals on the downhill road they installed a runaway berm of loose material eight feet wide, 100 feet long and approximately 4 feet high. Although the berms have never been used, they were designed to stop any of the giant carriers whose brakes had failed and were intended for use in conjunction with standard runaway ramps. They serve as a constant reminder of the emphasis placed on employee safety.

Mojave's precalciner greatly increased production capacity and efficiency.

Mojave Cement is transported in bulk.

CONCRETE-CEMENT

CATALINA PACIFIC

"...a new corporation with a notable history..."

Catalina Pacific Concrete doesn't manufacture cement, it delivers concrete. Ready mix trucks sporting the distinctive grey, red and blue diamond symbol of Catalina Pacific Concrete leave 13 sites throughout Southern California on their daily delivery routes. They represent the youngest branch of the California Portland Cement family, but can trace their history back to the early part of the Twentieth Century.

Catalina Pacific Concrete was created and incorporated when Onoda Cement obtained California Portland Cement from CalMat Co. late in 1990. CalMat had been formed by the merger of California Portland Cement Company and Conrock. Cal Portland manufactured cement and Conrock was an aggregate, asphalt and ready mix company.

When the merger split up and Onoda Cement purchased California Portland, Onoda also acquired the batch plants and ready mix trucks which provided the physical base for Catalina Pacific Concrete. The personnel base came from nearly 300 teamsters, operating engineers and machinists who chose to join the new company. Some of the drivers such as Harry Delre could count membership in the million mile safety club as one of their achievements.

Alfred Gomez, Chuck Crowley, Earl W. Smith and Ronald Davis could all be found on the list of people associated with Catalina Pacific who had been driving ready mix trucks and operating batch plants for years prior to the formation of CalMat. They had seen trucks carrying the Conrock logo be repainted with the CalMat insignia after the merger and then with the new Catalina Pacific identification when the merger split up.

Some could recall that the more concise Conrock designation had come from the Consolidated Rock Products Company name, but few memories went back to the

Nearly 300 teamsters, operating engineers and machinists...

Alameda plant 1942.

West L.A. plant.

Catalina Pacific Mixer 1990.

Consolidated Rock Mixer 1935.

... Union, Consumers, and Reliance merging 1929.

origins of the sand and gravel companies which formed Consolidated Rock. Vern Pollard's family might well recall those early days, as his father was a long-time employee. His son represents the third generation to work for Catalina Pacific or its predecessor companies.

While the cement company had grown through plant expansion and modernization, the sand and gravel companies had expanded both through the acquisition of new sites and of other companies. Early company names such as "Union" and "Consolidated" clearly imply the joining together of more than one company. Union Rock Company, which traced its origins back to 1919, was a combination of over a dozen companies when it joined with Consumers Rock and Gravel and Reliance Rock Company to form the appropriately named Consolidated Rock Products Company.

The three companies, Union, Consumers and Reliance, had been brought together in 1929 by the Pacific Mutual Life Insurance Company investment group. Consolidated Rock Products, the new company, commanded a major share of the rock products business in its market area.

It was the first company in Southern California to develop ready mix trucks in the early 1930's. Ready mix trucks did not come already assembled in those days. Some

GROWTH / CHANGE

1919	Union Rock Company began
1929	Consolidated Rock Products Company formed from Union, Reliance and Consumers
1932	First ready mixed concrete delivered
1962	California Materials acquired by Consolidated Rock Products Co.
1972	Consolidated Rock becomes Conrock
1984	Conrock and California Portland Cement merge to form CalMat
1990	Catalina Pacific Concrete incorporated

existing Pierce Arrow dump trucks had been modified to accommodate the mobile mixer. Once the conversion was made, it was time to begin deliveries.

The first ready mix came from what is now the Alameda batch plant. Alameda played a major role in ready mix production because it was a prime aggregate source and not solely a batch plant.

Of the thirteen current Catalina Pacific batch plants, five can be traced back to the early years of development. In addition to Alameda the list includes Canoga, Wilmington, and rather sedate Home Junction (west Los

This 1947 Wilimington batch plant crew could still find their way around the current facility.

Angeles) and the far more rambunctious "Wahoo", later to be Rosco and then Sun Valley.

Prior to the development of ready mix, the component parts of concrete — cement, rock and sand — had been trucked to a construction site separately. A divided bed dump truck would provide the components in the approximate proper proportions, but it was up to the contractor to do the actual mixing. This often resulted in a less than uniform product. Ready mix provided for a much better quality control.

A second major innovation attributed to the companies which formed Consolidated was the introduction of washed sand and aggregate and the sale of the same by weight rather than volume. This too provided a much higher quality product, as the impurities were largely eliminated and the quantity delivered was much more usable. Buildings which used the concrete were much more stable.

Consolidated Rock had long been a customer of California Portland Cement and the relationship grew even closer in the decade of the '30's when CPC acquired about 30% of Consolidated's stock. The relationship remained, however, that of two business organizations. California Portland had many other ready mix customers and was careful not to give preferential treatment or prices to Consolidated.

Catalina Pacific Concrete works to meet specific needs.

Durbin (now Baldwin Park) plant batch control room.

Prior to ready mix the ingredients for concrete were mixed at the site.

Catalina Pacific Concrete, a subsidiary of CPC, works closely with its customers and engineers from commercial testing laboratories to meet the specific needs of each phase of construction projects. Concrete is tested at the job site by inspectors to assure the correct slump has been achieved.

Strength test results are compared with the design strength and the mix design for the concrete is modified as necessary. To help guarantee that strength requirements are met, Catalina Pacific uses a computer program to generate the correct mixture designs and batching proportions are automatically transferred to the computer used for dispatching ready mix deliveries.

Catalina Pacific's commitment to quality concrete can be seen by a visit to its fully-equipped concrete laboratory. Test batches of concrete are prepared in the laboratory to evaluate new mix designs and to monitor the performance of cements, aggregates, and admixtures (additives). The laboratory staff includes technicians certified by the American Concrete Institute and senior personnel who are certified Concrete Technologists, adhering to National Ready Mix Concrete Association standards.

In addition to conducting quality control testing on raw materials, the laboratory staff provides on-the-job quality control during concrete delivery, and the lab works closely with the batch plants to continuously improve concrete quality.

Catalina Pacific can claim a distinguished heritage. It is a new corporation with a notable history. It holds a major portion of the business in its market area, operates over 200 ready mix trucks from the 13 Southern California sites with a capacity of 20,000 cubic feet delivered daily. It is a new company built upon a firm foundation in the industry.

In 1922 this site was called Home Junction, by the mid-1980's it was called West Los Angeles and the surrounding area had changed as well.

CORPORATE PEOPLE

CORPORATE PEOPLE WERE USUALLY CLOSELY ASSOCIATED WITH THE LOS ANGLES OFFICE. Their concerns were with the corporate well being and while the production at the plant level certainly played a major part in the health of the corporation, it was not the only concern.

In general, these were the people who dealt with the larger financial matters. Often they were also the people who either personally provided funding for the continuation of the company or had access to such funding. This was particularly true in the early history of the corporation.

Some looking forward and looking back takes place in this section, but there is no single base period as is the case in the previous section. Once again the line is not clearly drawn between the corporate and production groups. Thomas Jefferson Fleming was the corporation Secretary for many years and at the same time General Manager for the plant.

Recognition should be given to those who provided support services for the directors and officers. They are not included in the focus of this section. Other functions such as sales and marketing, engineering and technical assistance also fell beyond the main scope of this presentation.

Individuals such as R.G. "Pat" Patterson, who headed the engineering staff for many years, and Sharon DeHayes, who directs the technical services function are representative of many others whose work is associated with the corporate office and are part of the *California Portland Cement* family.

At the directorate level, family relationships tended to be personal. Directors in the twentieth century often married into the family or were direct decendents of Mr. Fleming or his associate Dan Murphy.

In the three decades between 1960 and 1990, both the family involvement and the family feeling toward the enterprise continued, but the corporation found itself in a much less family oriented world. It had grown large enough to be noticed by those interested in the composition of corporations rather than the product produced.

California Portland Cement had followed the stream from the placid mountain lake, in which it was merely one of the fish comfortably surviving, to the ocean, in which it had to learn cohabitation with the sharks. The founding fathers would recognize neither their company nor the environment in which it functioned, but they would have recognized the need to adapt and continue. They were familiar with difficult times.

Chapter Two

CALIFORNIA PORTLAND
CORPORATE

"They were pioneers . . ."

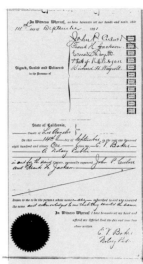

Articles of Incorporation were filed in Sept. 1891.

John P. Culver. . . Frank H. Jackson. . . Ernest Waycott. . . Richard H. Waycott. . . Harry R. O'Bryan. One by one they signed the incorporation papers. When they concluded, there remained only the filing with the County Clerk and the Secretary of State in Sacramento. The California Portland Cement Company was a reality. A century of producing portland cement West of the Rockies had begun.

Although the corporation was headquartered in Los Angeles, this began as a local venture. The Waycotts and Mr. O'Bryan listed San Bernardino as their address. Mr. Culver and Jackson listed Los Angeles. It was common at this time to have some local representation on corporation papers , while the major source of the funding was located in one of California's larger cities where financing was more readily available.

California Portland Cement had its principal investor, not a token representative, in San Bernardino. Ernest Waycott, with 2495 shares valued at $100 each, was clearly the largest stockholder in a corporation which listed a total capitalization of $500,000. The next largest shareholder was John Culver with 834. Jackson and O'Bryan each had 833 shares. Richard Waycott was a very minor participant with only 5 shares.

Creating the company and producing the product, however, were two entirely different tasks. The founding five felt they were capable of operating a major manufacturing plant. They were pioneers in the production of portland cement in Southern California, a long way from Pennsylvania's Lehigh Valley, the heart of the cement

industry in the United States. They were also intent upon producing portland cement, a variety which had yet to establish a firm hold on the United States market.

In 1891 there were only 16 plants manufacturing portland cement in the U.S. These plants provided fewer than 500,000 barrels of cement. The production of domestic natural cement in the same year reached over 7,700,000 barrels. The road to success was neither flat nor smooth.

Selecting a site for the plant was perhaps the easiest job. Marble had been quarried and cut at Mt. Slover at least as early as 1872. There was also evidence of bottle-shaped lime kilns at various locations on the mountain, which may have been used as early as the 1840's.

Just a few short months after the incorporation papers had been filed, the company obtained a five year lease of the Colton Lime Quarry, which had been operating on Slover Mountain, thereby guaranteeing a source of limestone.

A more difficult — and costly — task was assigned to the Waycotts and Mr. O'Bryan. They were responsible for the construction of the plant and the purchase of the equipment. They selected a location on the North side of Mt. Slover in Colton as the site for "Mill A".

Mr. Culver and Jackson were charged with furnishing the necessary knowledge needed for the manufacture of hydraulic cement. They were also to obtain exclusive access to the use of Dr. George Duryee's cement making and kiln patents.

One can assume Jackson and Culver — or one of the other directors — had some previous

Mt. Slover served as a source of marble and limestone before the cement plant was established.

knowledge of the cement industry. This assumption is based upon the dates of the Duryee patents. His patent for the manufacturing process had been granted in 1889 and that for a "Revolving Roasting Furnace," which can be readily recognized as a kiln, the following year.

Although all of the founders listed Southern California addresses, it seems likely that they had some connection with the cement industry. If they did not, it is unlikely they would have known of such recent developments as the Duryee patents, for the center of the industry was in the Lehigh Valley.

The partners were not pioneers in the sense of exploring and discovering a large mineral deposit. They were manufacturing pioneers whose goal was one hundred barrels of cement a day.

This required considerable capital to be invested in a plant. The Waycotts and O'Bryan were charged with building the facility, which they would in turn sell to California Portland Cement for stock. In 1894 the company obtained the plant from the three investors in exchange for the guarantee of payment of a debt. Presumably this debt had been acquired in conjunction with the construction of the plant.

The following year the Board of Directors agreed to pay George Duryee $1037.40, plus a royalty for each barrel of cement or lime produced, for the exclusive right to use his cement making process in Southern California. This was just for the use of the process. It did not include purchasing the kilns, crushers and other machinery, all of which had to be manufactured elsewhere and brought to the plant site.

Ernest Waycott was appointed General Manager and Superintendent of the works at Colton in 1894. He had the responsibility of making the plant productive. Given the amount of money he had invested, this was a sensible appointment. It was certainly in his best interest to see that the plant did well and he could boast of producing its first cement in that year.

GROWTH / CHANGE

1891	CPCC was incorporated
1894	Ernest Waycott appointed General Manager
1895	Company obtains rights to Duryee patents
1900	Stimson & Fleming receive contract
1901	"Dust nuisance" cases begin
1904	Murphy and Fleming join Board
1906	Dan Murphy elected President
1915	Neighbors Day held at Colton plant
1924	Thomas J. Fleming dies
	E.E. Duque appointed Secretary
1939	Dan Murphy dies. Duque elected President
1941	California Portland Cement's 50th year
1950	Stock split 10 for 1
1959	Richard A. Grant elected President
1970	Michael A Morphy elected President
1981	Stock split 2 for 1
1984	CPCC merges with Conrock–forms CalMat
1987	Brierly take over attempt at Conrock
1990	CPCC becomes part of Onoda Cement
	Catalina Pacific Concrete formed

While the major ingredient for the physical production of cement — limestone — could be found in Mt. Slover, the major ingredient for going into the cement business — money — was not as easily located. Early minutes of the Board of Directors are full of requests for loans, attempts to find sources of funds and, finally, assessments on stock.

Construction on Mill A began in 1892. Quarry rock was sent down the covered chute seen to the left of the stack.

"...we are beginning to know a little about this business ourselves."

New sources of funds often resulted in new faces on the Board. In July 1894 the company obtained a loan of $10,000 from "Toberman & Little", using the plant and property at Colton as security for the one year note.

Later the same year S.W. Little appears as a member of the Board of Directors and J.R. Toberman is elected the first Secretary-Treasurer, a position which had been separate prior to that time.

Ernest Waycott was President, a significant stockholder and of some significance in the management structure. Board minutes of July 9, 1894 state "The President being absent and no statement having been received from the factory owing to R.R. Strike the meeting was adjourned..." Waycott made it to Los Angeles the following day and the Board met.

By the following year, it was clear that the Board was adding some definition to the structure and the operational philosophy. It was also clear that they would not rely entirely on their own pocketbooks. An 1895 resolution stated, "...that it is for the best interest of said Company to borrow from time to time such amounts as may be necessary and convenient for the purpose of carrying on its business..."

Ultimately, the Board found it necessary to resort to an assessment on the stock. Perhaps the resolution on borrowing was related to the fact that the deadline for payment of the $1.00 per share assessment, established in 1894, had to be extended five times before the Board could feel secure.

Even this was not very much security. Additional loans were obtained and additional fees assessed the stockholders.

Finally, it became too much for Ernest Waycott. The first assessment of $1.00 per share, "Payable immediately in Gold Coin" had taken effect in early 1894. It was followed by assessment number two in February 1895 for $1.00 per share. On June 12, 1895 a third assessment was authorized. This time it was $2.00 per share.

Ernest Waycott, Superintendent and General Manager of the Company works at Colton, major shareholder and Vice President of the Company, had run out of resources.

In a petition to the Board of Directors he explained that the financial backing he had expected would not be forthcoming. His backers, who were in British Columbia, had suffered a severe setback when fire destroyed their lumber mills. They had no funds to loan others.

Waycott asked for some relief from the assessment and stressed "That this is a very critical time in the history of this Company and I consider that the success of this concern depends largely on the way things are managed for the next few months at the mill..."

His communication to the Board expressed his confidence in the future of the endeavor, "One great reason for my faith is that we are beginning to know a little about this business ourselves and shall not have to be governed by what others say so much in the future."

Nonetheless, Waycott made his personal position quite clear. "...if my stock goes all interest in the concern goes with it, for my salary cuts no figure [Waycott drew a salary of $100 a month as General Manager], because I would not work a moment longer than it took you to get a man to fill my place, if I lose my stock."

While the Board was able to grant Ernest Waycott some relief from the assessment, they evidently took him quite literally at his word. When he submitted his resignation as Superintendent at the September 25, 1895 meeting, it was accepted, with three directors voting for it and one not listed in the vote.

Waycott's subsequent motion to have the resignation withdrawn died for lack of a second. Director Jackson moved that F.N. Spear be named Superintendent and that he be put in charge at once. The motion carried. It had not taken the Board long to find a man to fill Waycott's place.

Waycott continued to be listed as a Director of the Company for the remainder of the year, although he was not always in attendance at the meetings. By the annual stockholders meeting in January 1896, Ernest Waycott is no longer listed as a shareholder.

During the first five years of the corporation's life, he

The Waycotts' departure... changed the corporate balance

had been the initial major stock holder, President and later Vice President of the Company, Superintendent and General Manager of the plant. By January 1897 he had petitioned the Superior Court in San Bernardino to be declared an insolvent debtor. In June of the previous year Richard H. Waycott had filed a similar petition.

Both Waycotts were involved with the development of the cement plant and that was evident from the list of debtors, some of whom appeared on both Richard's and Ernest's petitions:

Debtor/Product	Amt.	Location	Date
Stearns Mfg. Co. Machinery	$3600	Colton, CA	1894
Wilcox & Rose Merchandise	$ 210	Colton, CA	1894
Union Lime Co. Merchandise	$ 225	Los Angeles	1894

The list is two pages long and includes such items as lumber, labor and fire brick. Many of these bills were undoubtedly related to the work at the Colton plant.

By 1897, of course, neither Richard or Ernest Waycott was associated with California Portland Cement Company and the financial woes of former directors, even founding directors, were not necessarily those of the company.

The departure of the Waycotts from the Board of Directors and that of H.R. O'Bryan, who had left earlier, changed the corporate balance from San Bernardino County to Los Angeles. O'Bryan was the company's first salesman, having been appointed in 1894, but he did not appear as a director after 1895.

By mid-1900 the shift from Colton to Los Angeles was completed with the establishment of the Farmers & Merchants Bank of Los Angeles as the Treasurer for the corporation. Some funds would return to Colton for incidental use at the plant and the company would remain an important economic contributor to the local community, but the corporation was firmly established in Los Angeles. Members of the Board of Directors would increasingly be drawn from the Los Angeles business community.

Frank Jackson, who had listed his residence as Los Angeles on the original Articles of Incorporation, witnessed the shift in location. He served as Vice President, Secretary and a member of the Executive Committee during his tenure on the Board of Directors.

He was the only member of the founding five to remain a director after the turn of the century. As such he was active at the time the original marketing contract with

California Portland Cement maintained an account at the First National Bank in Colton, but its primary banking association was in Los Angeles.

There were ties to the banking and business community.

Fleming & Stimson was negotiated in 1900. He resigned from the Board a week before Fleming was elected a director.

Thomas Jefferson Fleming, while not a founding director, is probably the name most prominent among the early leaders of the company. It is tempting to view him as the patriarch of the California Portland Cement corporate family. The husbands of both his daughter and grand daughter, became presidents of the company (E.E. Duque and Richard A. Grant). Another son-in-law (Asa V. Call) served as a long term director. A grandson, (Thomas Fleming Call), and a great grandson (Richard A. Grant, Jr.) served independent terms of over a decade.

In addition, it was Fleming who persuaded Daniel J. Murphy to provide financial backing for a reorganized California Portland Cement Company. Murphy served as president for 35 years and his name remained associated with the Board of Directors for many years after his death through the participation of his daughter and ultimately the Dan Murphy Foundation.

The family linkages were obvious. What is not quite so obvious to the casual viewer is that these are people who traveled in the same business and social circles. At times it might be difficult to separate the business from the social aspects of their lives.

Businessman's clubs, such as the California Club, tended to provide a social atmosphere in which members and guests could gather and either retreat from or conduct business, as they chose. It was a more casual atmosphere in which to negotiate deals and contracts. It was understood that the first contacts with the Miller family of Oregon, which as late as 1979 held a 10% interest in California Portland, took place at the California Club many years earlier.

Both Fleming and Daniel Murphy were members of the California Club, which listed Thomas L. Duque, E.E. Duque's father, as one of its founders.

It is reasonable to expect that some of the social contacts which were nourished at the clubs should carry over into family social life and ultimately result in marriage between the business families. One may assume the personal relationships also tended to improve business relationships.

Furthermore, company directors tended to be those who owned stock in the corporation and stock was relatively limited. It was natural that what stock existed would be shared with other family members. Therefore, the leadership remained with a rather small number of people for many years.

Fleming is a pivotal figure in California Portland's history. He represents another step in the transition from those who established and built the initial plant, such as O'Bryan and Waycott, to the financial community of Los Angeles, which provided much of the leadership during the twentieth century.

This transition can be traced at least to the election of J.R. Toberman and S.H. Mott. Toberman, who was typical of this "second generation" of CPC directors, joined the Board in 1895 and Mott became a director three years later. They were involved in a number of business interests in addition to the production of cement in Colton. Mott was a founder of the Farmers and Merchants Bank.

During Toberman's term on the California Portland Board, he also became Treasurer of the Farmers and Merchants Bank. The same year he was named treasurer of the bank, 1900, he resigned as Treasurer of CPC and the bank was declared the official treasurer for the company.

In 1912 another link between the bank and the company was established. Thomas L. Duque, the father of Ernest Elroy Duque, a future president of CPC, had been quite active in the Los Angeles banking community during the later nineteenth and early twentieth centuries. In 1912 he became a director of the Farmers and Merchants Bank. Farmers and Merchants ultimately became part of the Security Pacific National Bank family and Security Pacific remained the primary bank for the cement company into the 1980's.

While Fleming may have focused on the production and marketing of cement, he clearly had important ties to the business and banking community. These were ties which would serve the company well.

By 1894 when the plant produced its first cement, the company was the largest manufacturing industry in the area. It was also almost constantly in need of funding.

Building the plant had been costly, as had obtaining the rights to the Duryee patents. Once that had been accomplished there still remained the problem of market-

. . ties served the company well.

M. A. MURPHY, MANAGER PORTLAND CEMENT COMPANY.

ing the product. Portland cement was not the only type available and even that portion of the market devoted to portland cement was dominated by the manufacturers in the East and in Europe.

While domestic production of portland cement increased significantly in the early part of this century, the chart below indicates how relatively insignificant it was in 1891.

AMERICAN CONSUMPTION OF CEMENT (BBLS)

Year	Domestic Natural	Domestic Portland	Imported Portland	Total
1891	7,768,000	454,000	2,988,00	11,210,000
1904	4.866.000	26,506,00	968,000	32,340,000
1910	1,139,000	76,550,000	307,000	77,996,000

The figures also provide a standard against which to measure the ambitious goals of the company's founders. They sought to build a plant which could produce not less than 100 barrels a day. In reality, the plant was listed in the 1913 "Directory of Cement Gypsum and Lime" as having a production run of 2,500 barrels annually.

The same directory lists Oro Grande Lime & Stone as one of six lime companies in California and the only one in the southern portion of the state. T.J. Fleming is listed as the president of the company with an address in the Stimson Building.

Mr. Fleming is noted in the directory as also being "Secy., Gen. Mgr., Pur Agt., and Sales Agt." for California Portland Cement Company, headquartered at Room 402 in the American Bank Building. A separate address is listed for Daniel Murphy, president of the company.

It was through the lime and stone company that Fleming and his partner W.H. Stimson became interested in the cement industry and California Portland Cement Company. In 1899 Willard Stimson had purchased a 1/2 interest in Fleming's lime and cement operation in Oro Grande, California — along with "one-half interest in four horses and their harnesses" and the tools and equipment used in the operation.

Oro Grande had been organized to mine, process and market limestone from deposits near Quartzite Mountain about three miles east of Oro Grande, California. It became an important distributor in the Los Angeles Area of not only its own product, but lime and cement from Colton as well.

In 1900 Fleming and Stimson were appointed agents for California Portland. Their territory was defined as Los Angeles and Pasadena. Macondry & Company was awarded

the territory north of Fresno. Oro Grande continued as the sole marketing agent for Colton lime until 1976 when it was replaced by the Colton Lime and Stone Co. After Fleming's death, his son-in-law, Asa Call, was elected president of Oro Grande.

Although the company had employed H.R. O'Bryan, one of the founders, as its first salesman in 1894 and had entered into a contract with Agua Fria Construction Company of Phoenix to serve as agents in Arizona the following year, the Fleming contract seems to be the first for agents in California.

If Thomas Fleming's interest in the cement business led him to look closely at the record of California Portland during its first six years of production, he found a very mixed record of success.

There had been some good years — which had at one

"It was the best of times . . ."

point even resulted in the plant running day and night to meet orders. There had also been some very trying financial times — which had resulted in the plant being closed during the last months of 1896.

There had been additional assessments on shares and, during the closing year of the Nineteenth Century, a few small dividends paid. Negotiations with Pacific Mutual Life Insurance Company had been undertaken to purchase the Colton Marble and Building Stone operation, thus providing room for expansion. Pacific Mutual had obtained the marble and building stone company in 1895 as the result of a court action.

The Board decided to authorize the issue of $80,000 in bonds and looked frequently for financial relief. Director S.W. Little seemed to be the man upon whom the "money gaze" often fell. He is mentioned several times as having loaned funds to the firm and is responsible for purchasing at least $20,000 of the bond issue.

Conflicts between the superintendent and the Chief Chemist had developed. By November of 1900 this situation had deteriorated to the point that the Secretary of the Board of Directors was instructed to write Edward Duryee, the Chief Chemist, and advise Mr. Duryee that "the Board of Directors have become aware of an apparent lack of Cooperation between the Chemist — and the Superintendent — and that they expect the Chemist will cooperate with the Supt. In every way, so as to make a perfect cement."

Duryee is an example of the central — and sometimes singular — role of the chemist. He was not the same Duryee who had patented the cement making process used by California Portland, but he was a respected cement chemist and it was the chemist who made sure the cement was good quality and properly mixed.

While his importance to the manufacturing of cement was clear, his accountability to the company was not. Duryee found himself in conflict with the Board of Directors over payment for his services. The Board felt obligated to withhold payment until certain records of the chemist's office were provided to the company. Duryee maintained these were his personal notes and not company property.

The conflict with Duryee over wages was eventually settled. The friction between the chemists and production people was something which continued for some time. At this point, it was probably aggravated by the fact that there were a series of plant superintendents, none of whom seemed to stay very long.

Duryee, nonetheless, is credited with applying his advanced knowledge of the cement making process to the operation at Colton and improving the quality. Michael A. Murphy of Colton was the Plant Superintendent when it reopened in August 1897 and was responsible for making some improvements in the methods of production.

Whatever the relationship between Murphy, who was also a member of the Board of Directors, and the chemist may have been, the quality of the cement began to improve. Murphy was able to report in January 1898 that continued research and improvements had resulted in a

Thomas Jefferson Fleming served as Secretary and General Manager of the company for over 20 years.

Colton Cement which had a greater tensile strength than any imported cement available.

Research had always been a standard of California Portland Cement. The founders recognized the need to know as much about modern methods as possible and sent representatives to the cement plants in the Eastern United States to gather information.

They purchased the rights to the cement making and kiln patents of Dr. George Duryee. These patents had been filed as late as 1891. They were clearly the most modern methods and equipment available.

In August 1900 the plant superintendent made an oral report to the Board and "expressed himself entirely in accord with the many suggestions made by Mr. Douglas who outlined many economies and systems practiced in up to date Eastern Portland Cement Factories."

Plant visitations continued under Fleming's leadership in the early Twentieth Century. He provided Wilson Hanna with letters of introduction to cement people throughout the country, asking them to show Hanna around their plants.

The practice of always looking for the most modern and efficient methods has continued through the company's one hundred years of existence. When new equipment and new plants were authorized, company people traveled throughout the country, as well as to Europe and Asia, to view the latest technological advances in operation.

Research has also been conducted on a regular basis at the laboratory. The company continues to maintain a research facility and can point with pride to the develop-

Wilson C. Hanna's tenure with California Portland spanned nearly six decades.

Action was ordered to provide a more frequent and more accurate inventory in the future. However, it was not the amount of cement on hand, but rather the quality of that cement which proved to be the most immediate problem facing the new General Manager and the Chemist.

Whatever the correct inventory might be in 1904, it represented cement which could not be used. Wilson Hanna described it as "green cement". He had been appointed chemist in June, 1904 and soon discovered warehouses full of defective cement. "My first report to Mr. Fleming was that there was nothing that I would ship."

Mr. Fleming agreed with Hanna. They would not ship inferior cement. The company's reputation had been severely damaged by the product already shipped under Dr. Neu's tenure. A month after Hanna's appointment to his new position, the plant closed. From July 1904 until the end of January, 1905 the plant made no clinker.

There was activity at the site, however. The existing cement was mixed and some re-ground until it met company specifications. Finding just the right mixture was a difficult task for a chemist who was just learning the business. Hanna, at one point, offered to resign his position in order to get an expert on cement to take his place. Mr. Fleming rejected the suggestion, noting that an "expert" had gotten them into this position in the first place.

That expert, Dr. Neu, had been providing Hanna with instructions on the making of cement, and Hanna had paid for this instruction with a significant part of his wages. After Dr. Neu left for a position with a cement company in New York, Hanna discovered the texts he had been purchasing through Neu actually belonged to the California Portland

ment of some speciality cements which came from their research.

Thomas Fleming was also personally involved with research at the plant. In 1911 he was responsible for the development of the Fleming Dust Control System. He had progressed from being merely an agent for the company to a position of prominence. With his election in 1904 as Secretary and General Manager added to his seat on the Board of Directors, he was in a position to have a significant impact on company affairs.

If Charles Dickens, the English author, had looked at the company's fortunes in 1904, he may well have described them with his famous quote about the French Revolution, "It was the best of times, it was the worst of times." It was a good year for the future of California Portland Cement as both Thomas J. Fleming and Wilson C. Hanna assumed key positions with the company. The year itself, however, was a low point in Cal Portland's history.

The first three years of the new century had witnessed the purchase of a new ball mill, a new grit mill, 100 acres of clay deposits near Perris, an increase in the number of employees to 130, the installation of a rock crushing plant and plant assets which soared to $1,000,000. The first few months of 1904 had been characterized by low sales, slow collections and the need for additional funds.

The problems were not helped any by the revelation at the September 1903 Board meeting that the inventory was not correct. Indeed, it had been overestimated by nearly one third. Actual stock was reported to be 23,332 barrels and not the 33,328 1/2 which had been carried on the inventory.

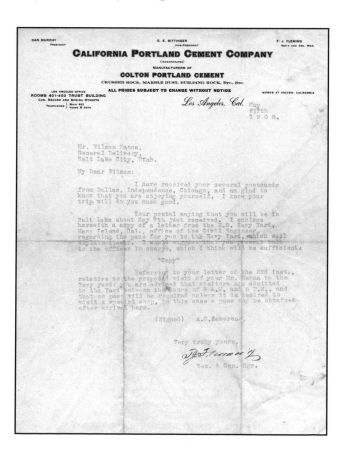

Directors met and dined at the Anderson Hotel.

Cement Company and not the good doctor.

At one point only Hanna, who was now without his "tutor," but had access to the company library, and Charley Burley, the night watchman were working at the site.

Progress was being made. It was possible to develop cement which met company standards. Some of this was provided to "Scotty" McNair to replace, at company expense, the defective sidewalks which had been poured in Colton. Some went to fill the orders which Fleming would obtain from time to time.

Fleming referred to this period in the company's history as "The Sinking Ship."

The "ship" clearly did not sink during the last half of 1904. Production resumed the following year and during January 1906 the company records indicated production of 10,095 barrels and shipment of 10,897.

Sidewalks were not the only thing in Colton built with cement manufactured on the slopes of Mt. Slover. One of the city's major hotels, the Anderson, had also been constructed with Colton Cement. The Board of Directors, headed by the recently elected President Dan Murphy, was in Colton in 1906 and was honored with the first dinner served in the Anderson Hotel.

The roller coaster which the cement industry rides was rising for California Portland at this time. It went from having only two employees on the site to having so many orders that cement was shipped as fast as Hanna would release it. He even suggested raising the price in order to scare away a few customers — and Fleming actually did raise it.

When times are good it is natural to think

of expansion. Late in 1906 Fleming and Hanna began laying plans for a new plant, Mill B. This was only the preliminary step. Fleming sought help from the experienced cement people in the East. He traveled to the Eastern United States with photos of the site, samples of the raw materials, the finished product and an analysis file with him.

Additional planning was completed with the assistance of Prof. R.C. Carpenter of Cornell University. E.W. Miller came to Colton as the engineer on the construction project and by November 1907 one of the five kilns in Mill B was in operation.

Just as Mill B was being completed, the economy declined and so did business. As Hanna remembers it this provided plenty of time for the cement users to "Knock Colton" for the poor cement which had been produced in 1904.

Something was needed to convince the buyers that California Portland Cement was now a fine quality product. Daniel Murphy and Thomas Fleming were businessmen and knew how to market a product.

The Board of Directors was among the first to dine at the new Anderson Hotel in Colton.

. . . at one time, only Hanna and Charley Burley were working . . .

The Southern California Chapter of the American Institute of Architects was meeting in November 1908. Murphy and Fleming arranged to have the entire group brought by train to the Colton plant where they were provided a banquet and a long presentation by Mr. Hanna, Colton's Chief Chemist, on the manufacturing and testing of cement.

Although he was relatively new in the profession, Hanna was beginning to earn respect. At the International Association For Testing Materials Sixth Triennial Congress, held in New York City in 1912, Hanna was providing written responses to and commenting on presentations by experts from around the world.

The architects meeting was a generally acclaimed success. It may have laid the groundwork for an even larger public event — the 1915 Get Acquainted Day barbecue. That event brought 3500 people to the plant and garnered headlines in the San Bernardino Daily Sun, which proclaimed "FEAST CEMENTS VALLEY FELLOWSHIP" The newspaper's front page picture on November 12th featured Margaret Fleming and Helen Duque sharing a collage with a sea of automobiles parked by the happy picnickers and the massive kilns.

Russian troops were reported as having landed in Rumania and Britain was considering compulsory recruitment to meet its needs in World War I, but the majority of the front page was devoted to the activities at Mt. Slover where the "Great Barbecue Acquaints People With Industry."

This was a well-planned and executed event. Instructions were provided for those attending and for plant personnel, who were asked to "work together and see that every visitor is carefully guarded from harm."

"'FEAST' CEMENTS VALLEY FELLOWSHIP"

Nearly two years later, on July 4, 1917, Fleming initiated one of his most memorable public events. The United States had entered World War I and Fleming had received permission to fly the nation's flag atop Mt. Slover day and night, with the flag illuminated after dark. Newspaper headlines proclaimed, "Thousands of Visitors Throng Hub City and Participate in Observance of Independence".

Accounts in the San Bernardino Daily Sun enthusiastically noted, "This great flag... was haloed against the sky by a great battery of electric scintillators, emphasizing the brilliancy of the red, the white and the blue in silhouette against the darkened background of the heavens."

The flag continued to provide inspiration for years to come. Writing to the company in 1934, Donald H. McIntosh stated, "From my office window in the Colton Union High School, of which I am the Principal, I have a full view of the mountain. It has been an inspiration to turn from my work at my desk and see 'Old Glory' floating at the mast

GET ACQUAINTED

WITH THE

Colton Cement Plant

Inspection 10 a. m. to 1 p. m.

QUALITY UNSURPASSED · COLTON PORTLAND CEMENT · ALWAYS UNIFORM

BARBECUE 1 P. M. to 2:30 P. M.

Neighbors' Day

THURSDAY, November 11, 1915

California Portland Cement Co.

LOS ANGELES   COLTON

WE BID YOU WELCOME!

Neighbors, friends, wellwishers, the California Portland Cement Company bids you welcome on this Get Acquainted Day. With our plant approximately complete as to its present units, we are glad to have you all come and see what has been accomplished, for we are all partners in the prosperity of this, our home county.

The danger to the casual visitor, the impracticability of having guides always at hand and the necessity for extreme care, combine to make it wise to keep our doors closed while the plant is running. But neighborly interest is not idle curiosity, and it is with pleasure that we find so many friends making this informal inspection.

Ten years ago the present management took control of this property. The making of cement had been going on about the same length of time previously, never with great success. Today our output is ten times as great as then. In the plants you have visited you have seen no machine which does not represent the highest development in this industry, some even a step in advance. Maintaining the present rate of production, this plant will have manufactured in the year 1915 as much cement as was produced in the entire United States in 1896, while this month alone will see an output equal to that of 1883.

With the improvement in methods and machinery has come greater demand. Every day the countryside rings with the blasts of giant powder, as the mountain is compelled to yield its riches. It is Industry's salute to the Gods of Commerce, and tells every neighbor that all is well.

It is well for neighbors to know each other, for then will they judge fairly and esteem rightly. Again we bid you welcome.

BARBECUE

Hosts—California Portland Cement Company.
Reception Committee—Colton Chamber of Commerce, Merchants' Association and J. Swinnerton.
Master of the Feast—William Starke.
Colton's Fellowship—R. M. McHargue.
San Bernardino's Appreciation—Ralph Swing.
Neighborly Welcome—E. M. Boyd.

Neighbors' Day was also known as "Get Acquainted Day" and served to acquaint people from throughout Southern California with the California Portland Cement Company.

Fleming Dust Control System was installed in 1911

Mill B was the first company facility on the south side of Mt. Slover.

head, high on the mountain top."

The company's "good neighbor" policy which was evident in the barbecue and flag raising had been strained in the first decade of the century. The problem was cement dust which was emitted from the kilns and was viewed as detrimental by the orange growers in the area.

Board minutes include mention of the problem as early as July 1901 when the Secretary was "instructed to notify the Gen. Foreman to abate the dust nuisance complained of by our neighbors." Eliminating the problem, however, was not quite that easy.

The citrus growers continued to complain and began to take their complaints to the courts. The completion of Mill B only served to intensify the problem. It was not a problem found only at the Colton plant. It was a problem for all cement plants.

It became a major problem for the company when the judge ruled against them in Hulbert v. California Portland Cement Company. Initially filed in 1909 the case was decided two years later and the company was ordered to cease production in Mill B and limit production in Mill A to 88,706 barrels. (It was estimated that the plant had produced 145,323 barrels of cement in 1907).

The judgement actually ordered Mill B closed until such time as something could be done about the dust problem. It seems the company did not close the mill, because it claimed it was working on the dust problem.

Fleming was experimenting with a system of blowers which would push the exhaust from the stacks through a series of water baffles and reclaim much of the dust. He had investigated other systems, including one which was being tested at nearby Riverside Cement, but that was still in the testing stage and Colton needed something proven.

The initial tests proved successful and the ultimate result was the Fleming Dust Collecting System which was installed on all kilns by November 1911. It removed and recovered a major portion of the dust and remained the principal dust control system, with modifications and improvements for many years.

It did not completely solve the problem of cement dust and, as the plant expanded, the dust problem expanded also. Concerns for cement dust falling on the city continued into the 1950's and beyond.

Company groves at the base of Mt. Slover produced prize winning citrus.

Construction of the collecting system also did not stop the law suits, some of which were not settled until 1915. Many of these legal actions were handled by Wesley Beach, who had been a boyhood friend of Wilson Hanna and represented the citrus growers. The friendship was destroyed by the legal battles.

Hanna notes that these actions also had a negative effect on Mr. Fleming, whom he describes as being "never the same again, although he made a brave effort." Hanna, himself, traced the origin of his white hair to the encounters and revealed that a doctor had told him "to go to another location."

He did not go and, probably somewhere in the midst of the legal actions, found himself working for a company which had citrus groves of its own. By 1916 the company was winning prizes at the National Orange Show, including a first for the largest oranges and a second for the greatest variety of citrus fruit displayed. It continued to grow citrus for several decades.

Being a good neighbor and the largest manufacturing firm in the neighborhood at times placed the company in an uncomfortable position. Its role as a major employer was illustrated by the cement dust court cases in which it was stipulated the company employed about 500 men, most of whom lived in Colton, which was a community of nearly 5000 at the time. By the early 1920's the company payroll had increased to over 900 men.

It was a large company in a small town and as such a convenient target for some. At various times there were attempts to extend the city limits or the limits of fire protection districts to include the plant and thereby increase tax revenue. There were occasional questions about just how much the company contributed to the community. In March 1925, the Mercury of Colton carried an editorial complaining about the lack of Colton Cement being used to pave city streets. It stated the company's product was shipped away, "some of it even to Europe."

The editorial brought an immediate response. An editorial in the competing Colton Courier emphasized the bright future of Colton, and noted that to the best of its knowledge, all the concrete in city streets had been mixed with Colton Cement. It suggested, however, that while the city had dutifully supported the plant, the company had not been supportive of the city.

A special meeting of the Chamber of Commerce was called and a resolution passed praising the company and refuting the newspaper's position. The Mercury of Colton retreated with a front page article headlined, "California Portland Cement Industry of Great Value To Colton." It closely followed the wording of information developed by the company and the editor admitted he had been a friend of Mr. Fleming.

Within the company memos and suggested responses had been considered. They provide an interesting insight into California Portland Cement's involvement with the local community.

While the issue of extending the city limits to include the plant was avoided, the response did point out that the company owned a large amount of

The Fleming Dust Collection system

Fleming's dust collection system — installed partially as a response to area citrus growers.

... the company had increased to over 900 men.

American Legion Post 155 promoted Colton's paved streets on a float built with financial support from the cement company.

acreage on which it paid taxes to the city. It also had donated cement for the tennis courts in the city park, had helped all the recently built churches in the city through donations of cement, donated cement for the recent construction of the Woman's Club. It was also a frequent and generous subscriber to local fund raising efforts.

California Portland Cement had furnished $500 for the "box car" float used by the local American Legion at its San Francisco meeting. The float had earned first prize for the most interesting exhibit in the parade.

The response claimed that 96% of the money paid for labor at the plant went to employees living in Colton. It was assumed this was contributed to the local economy, as many of the workmen lived in the city and owned their own homes.

The company also spent its money in Colton, having purchased $39,000 in goods from the local merchants in the previous year. They even bought their postage stamps in the city — and mailed them to the Los Angeles office. Unlike some other large employers, California Portland had no commissary, thereby funneling all purchases made by employees to the local businessmen.

Furthermore, the company was the city's best advertiser. All the cement sacks stated "Colton Cement" in bold lettering. No other local industry could provide such wide spread advertising.

Two years after the newspaper editorials, in June 1927, Fleming Park was donated to the city as a memorial to Thomas J. Fleming. It is perhaps significant the park had a

stage and band shell. One of the things the company had helped fund was the Colton Band.

A larger park, designated Veterans Memorial Park complete with landscaping and baseball diamond was donated in South Colton in 1939. Contributions to the community continued through the years with plant employees being involved in local activities. An article in the Colton Daily Courier in 1936 related, "...employees of the Colton cement plant are among the most influential of Colton citizens, serving the city in various capacities in its social and recreational life. Two of them are members of the city council."

The company, in later years, has even donated some large pieces of Mt. Slover for commemorative plaques. One is outside Whitmer Auditorium and another at the high school football stadium.

Although the corporate offices were in Los Angeles, company officers did not manage the enterprise from a distance. Mr. Fleming was well known at the plant. His death in 1924 marked the end of the company's transition from infancy to adulthood. It would always be subject to the fluctuations in the economy, but it was now a full-fledged cement company not just a fledgling corporation with a cement plant.

Expansion in the early 1920's had brought kiln 9 into operation and the very month in which Fleming was buried, March 1924, the company set a record for clinker production — 250,000 barrels.

W.H. Stimson was Fleming's business partner and had joined him on the Board of Directors in 1903. It was Fleming's friend Daniel Murphy, however, who provided the infusion of money needed to keep the corporation on an even financial keel during that troubled time. Murphy was elected President in 1904 and continued in that capacity for over three decades.

He was a businessman and community leader with experience in the mercantile business and ties to the oil industry. He was also a philanthropist who had been

Fleming's Death marked the end of transition.

Ernest Elroy Duque was elected President in 1939.

appointed a Commander of the Equestrian Order of the Holy Sepulcher by Pope Pius XI in 1931.

For the last 15 years of his presidency he was teamed with E.E. Duque, who had succeeded Fleming as Secretary and General Manager. The company prospered during the late 1920's. Very few companies prospered during the following decade of the 1930's. The Great Depression left its mark throughout the country and the cement industry was not spared.

It is to Mr. Murphy's and Mr. Duque's credit that California Portland Cement survived the economic hard times, continued to operate the plant, and even managed to regularly pay dividends to the shareholders.

Although the times were difficult, the Board and Officers of the company remained active in obtaining what work was available and in planning for the future, when money would be available. They sought out sites for potential expansion into Arizona and provided cement for such projects as Hoover Dam, the All American Canal, the Metropolitan Water aqueduct, Union Station in Los Angeles, and various highway projects. In addition the company shipped Colton cement to the U.S. Navy for use in construction in Hawaii and the South Seas.

Daniel Murphy died in September 1939 at the age of 83. He was the last member of the California Portland Cement Board of Directors who had experienced Mr. Fleming's "Sinking Ship" period.

Other members on the Board in 1939 included J.R. Chandler, a partner in the firm which had handled the early dust control cases, who had joined the Board in 1911 and L.E. Bancroft who had replaced W.H. Stimson in 1927. T.J. Murphy had filled Fleming's seat in 1924. Asa Call had begun his initial term on the Board in 1927 and L.R. McFie had joined the Board in 1932. Call was associated with the Pacific Mutual Life Insurance Company, which had obtained shares in the company in compensation for the purchase of the Colton Lime and Building Stone properties at Mt. Slover early in the company's history.

Mr. Murphy's passing represented a milestone in the company's history. The most immediate change on the Board of Directors was the election of his 35-year-old daughter, Bernardine, to the Board. Later Mrs. Bernardine Murphy Donohue, she was the first woman to serve as a director. A woman stockholder, Mrs. J.M. Woodville, had been listed as early as 1903 and the Fleming daughters later held stock in their own names, although their father held their proxy..

Women would have to wait until the late 1950's, however, before they would gain employment at the plant sites, although they had staffed the corporate office prior to

Fleming Park – donated in 1927

Family ties were strong

WEDDING BELLS RING FOR SOCIETY COUPLE

Leaving the Church of Our Lady of Carmel in Montecito, Mr. and Mrs. Richard Angus Grant are shown above a few moments after their marriage in a beautiful setting.
Robert Veight photo

DOROTHY DUQUE AND GRANT WED IN MONTECITO CHURCH
BY CHRISTY FOX

Actors Ballot on Radio St
Hollywood Vot

that time. They would not be members of production crews at the plants until the mid-1970's. Women who usually worked in the offices did find themselves operating some of the large plant equipment on a short term basis during the strike action in 1981.

1939 had been an eventful year for Ernest Elroy Duque. It began with the wedding of his daughter Dorothy to Richard A. Grant and concluded with his election as President of the California Portland Cement Company.

The January wedding had been held in Our Lady of Mount Carmel Church in Montecito. Archbishop John J. Cantwell read the marriage ceremony. It was an event which made the social pages of the Los Angeles Times and was to continue a long line of family relationships on the Board of Directors for the California Portland Cement Company. The new Mrs. Grant's grandfather was Thomas J. Fleming.

The new President headed a company that was emerging from the economic depression of the 1930's, which had effectively restricted any major expansion. California Portland

looked forward to an outstanding decade in the 1940's.

By 1941, the fiftieth anniversary of the corporation, production had finally matched the peak year of 1928. With the entry of the United States into World War II in December 1941, the economic emphasis changed again.

Emphasis was placed on production to meet the nation's wartime needs, but the manpower needs of the Armed Services took their toll on the labor force at the cement plant. Management had to find ways to produce more cement with fewer men. At times this simply meant the same men worked more shifts. This was far from ideal, but it proved to be a period of very safe performance for the company.

With the shift to a peacetime economy, California Portland could begin to put into place some of the planning which had been on the shelf for years. The first project was expansion into the Arizona market. Additional surveys were taken of the market potential in 1947. These were sufficiently favorable to convince the majority of the Board of Directors it was time for the first completely new plant construction since the completion of Mill C over 30 years earlier.

Not all the directors felt favorably toward the project in a neighboring state, but Mr. Duque was adamant. This was a project which must be undertaken. By the April 1948 Board meeting approval had been given for the plant specifications and the expenditure of an estimated $3 million had been authorized.

Construction began at the Rillito, Arizona site late in the Spring of 1948 and was completed by October of the following year. December 1949 saw the initial shipment of Arizona Portland Cement.

Arizona Portland was a wholly owned subsidiary of California Portland. Its market area was largely Arizona and a sales office was maintained in Phoenix. Sales were so good that the Board authorized an additional $3 million for an expansion program which was begun in March 1951 and raised production capacity to 1,500,000 barrels a year.

Expansion to Mojave soon followed.

R.G.Patterson, far right, joined Directors L.R. McFie, A.L. McCall, E.R. Valentine, R.A. Grant, H.K. Bagley, and E.E. Duque,during 1956 Mojave inspection.

Directors remain active in planning for the future.

Expansion, modernization and improvement were the watchwords of the company for the next three decades. In the Fall of 1954 work was begun on the Mojave plant. With an estimated final cost of $12 million this plant began shipping bulk cement in January 1956. Mojave Cement had joined Arizona Cement and Colton Cement as the company's major products.

Expansion of the Mojave plant soon followed, along with improvements to existing facilities. The original plant at Colton was not forgotten. Mojave had been built because it had been determined that Colton would not be able to provide enough cement to meet projected demands, but Colton was scheduled for a complete modernization program.

By 1963, when the modernization at Colton was complete, the company could boast of having installed the first closed circuit industrial television system in the West at its Mojave plant and the most modern computer system in the cement industry at the Colton plant. All of these improvements, and those which continued to be made in the following 27 years, helped the company manufacture cement more efficiently.

No amount of advanced technology such as the preheater kiln installed at Rillito or the precalciner kiln at Mojave, or the new mills at Colton could totally compensate for the fact that the cement industry is closely tied to the construction industry and to the highs and lows of the general economy. Business and profits during this period remained a reflection of the changing economy, with the Annual Report of 1975 detailing a particularly low period.

Annual Reports, while noting the additions to plants and the modernization of equipment, continually highlighted the increasing costs of fuel, power and labor. In an attempt to use the most efficient and inexpensive fuel, plants were converted from natural gas to coal and provided with the means of using either coal, natural gas or fuel oil, depending upon which could be obtained most economically.

Consideration was constantly being given to methods of producing cement more efficiently and with less cost. Often this resulted in the installation of more advanced technological methods. The cogeneration plant at Colton was hailed as a significant advancement in reducing power expenditures.

California Portland Cement Company Board of Directors 1891-1984

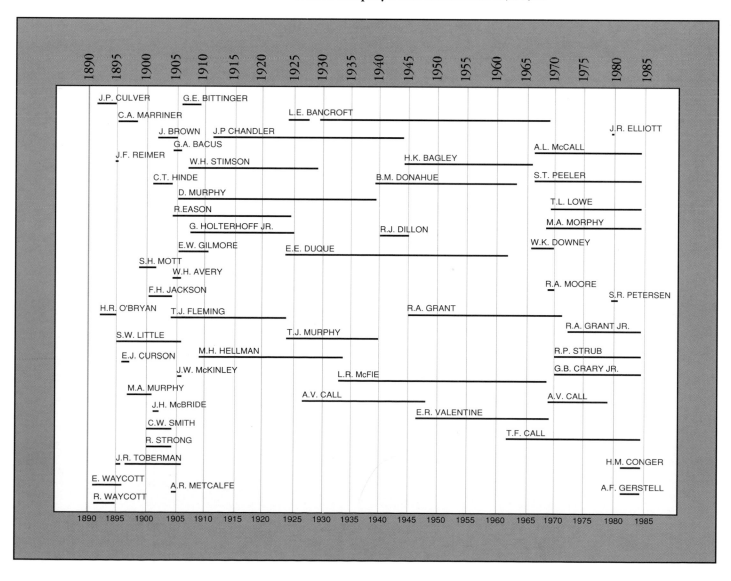

California Portland had been working to upgrade plants

The late 1970's were banner years for cement production in the company. In 1979 it even imported clinker to be ground at the plants. But the Annual Report of that year included segments for the previous two years which reflected the upswing in business while expressing caution that the cement industry was cyclical and more difficult times may be ahead.

The industry did not have to wait long. By the early 1980's the roller coaster on which the cement industry rides was heading down again. Looking back to a similar period in 1975, the 1982 Annual Report simply repeated the grim forecast which had been issued 7 years earlier.

Concern was also shown for the increasing amount of foreign cement which was making its way into the domestic market. Those with an eye toward history might have looked back at the company's beginnings and noted the competition with imported cement. There was a difference, however, the new imports were from Australia and Japan, not Europe.

Michael Morphy, who had been elected president of the company in 1970, stated in the 1980 Annual Report that the amount of imported clinker and cement had risen from 900,000 tons in 1959 to 9,300,000 in 1979. He went on to note the need for larger and more technologically advanced domestic plants, but cautioned that this would require "gigantic sums of money."

California Portland had been working to upgrade its plants and increase production. The new kiln at the Mojave plant, with its preheater calcining tower was an example of this approach. It would have been relatively easy to simply add another conventional kiln or two to Mojave and increase production.

The company chose to investigate the most modern technology, send representatives to Japan to view a preheater calcinating tower in operation, and even test the equipment with domestic materials which would be used at the Mojave plant. The result was a kiln which nearly doubled the original capacity of the plant, but only used 60% of

the energy required by the original.

Even increases in size and advances in technology could not completely save the domestic cement industry. European cement companies were viewing the American market and were increasingly interested in purchasing North American cement plants.

This was also the era of financial experts who often found the parts of a company more attractive than the whole and were interested in taking over a company to spin off individual parts.

California Portland had some experience being on the receiving end of a take over offer. It was surprised, however, when the trade papers announced in April 1979 that the Martin Marietta Corp. offered to purchase the stock of the Dan Murphy Foundation. The foundation was named for and had a direct relationship to the shares of Daniel Murphy, the former President of California Portland. It held approximately 30% of the stock in the company.

There was no follow up on the offer, but it did serve to remind the company that other corporations could be interested in its stock. Management's level of awareness was emphasized by some of the seminars it provided senior staff on this issue of takeovers.

California Portland Cement stock had increased in volume through the years. The company which began with 5000 shares valued at $100 each had, by 1920, increased the amount of outstanding stock to 20,000 shares. This soon rose to 30,000 and finally 50,000 before the end of the decade. It stayed at that level until September 1950 when the Board, with the consent of the shareholders, approved a 10 for 1 split, bringing the value to $10 a share. At the time of the split the fifty thousand shares were held by 502 shareholders.

Although available over the counter, the stock was not heavily traded. In 1970 the company took a major step away from its small

California Portland's sales force was noted for taking the most modern transportation available.

Those with an eye toward the future . . .

shareholder base when it joined the American Stock Exchange. Additional stock increases took place until, in the Spring of 1984, there were more than 7 million shares outstanding. This reflected the latest 2 for 1 split which had been approved in April 1981 as a means of increasing the marketability and availability of the stock on the American and Pacific stock exchanges.

On June 27, 1984 over 87% of the company's outstanding shares were voted in favor of a merger with Conrock Company. A new company name was to be selected after the merger. Ultimately the name became CalMat, a name to which Conrock had the rights as a result of having acquired the California Materials Company some years earlier.

Michael Morphy, now Chairman and Chief Executive Officer of CPC, opened the special shareholders meeting called to vote on the merger. It was held in the Bonaventure Hotel in Los Angeles, which had been constructed largely with California Portland Cement.

Shareholders, accustomed to annual reports which seldom contained more than 25 pages, had previously been provided a 150 page publication explaining the consolidation of the two firms. Chairman Morphy briefly summarized the reasons for the merger. He noted the advantages of broader capitalization and the difficulty of smaller companies competing successfully in the cement business and keeping up with expensive technological advances. He also suggested the merger would prove successful for the shareholders of both companies.

Mr. Frederick Gerstell, Cal Portland's president, added some additional reasons for joining with Conrock. He

mentioned the favorable financial position of the proposed new entity and the fact that it would broaden the product base. The marriage with Conrock brought with it not only the cement related activities, but also asphalt and solid-waste disposal land fills. The new company would also have significant real estate holdings which could be developed.

The merger was being proposed in a business climate which viewed vertical integration with some favor. This was a considerable change from the atmosphere of the 1940's and 1970's when the nation's cement companies had been accused of violating the federal anti-trust statutes.

Chairman Morphy took time at the conclusion of the meeting to briefly relate the history of California Portland Cement and note that some of the children, grandchildren and great grandchildren of the company's early leaders were in attendance at the shareholders meeting.

In making the introductions of the directors at the beginning of the meeting Morphy had noted the long term relationship several of them had with the company. He could also have mentioned both a grandson and great grandson of Thomas J. Fleming were members of the Board of Directors.

The company had maintained the family connection and feeling even with the increased amount of stock

California Portland Cement Co. and Conrock Co.
are pleased to announce
the combination of the two companies
was completed on June 27, 1984

The name of the new company is

CalMat Co.

William Jenkins
Chairman of the Board
and Chief Executive Officer

A. Frederick Gerstell
President and
Chief Operating Officer

Business offices are located at

California Portland Cement Div.
9300 Flair Drive
El Monte, CA 91731
(213) 680-2316

Conrock Div.
3200 San Fernando Road
Los Angeles, CA 90065
(213) 258-2777

CalMat was the name selected after the merger.

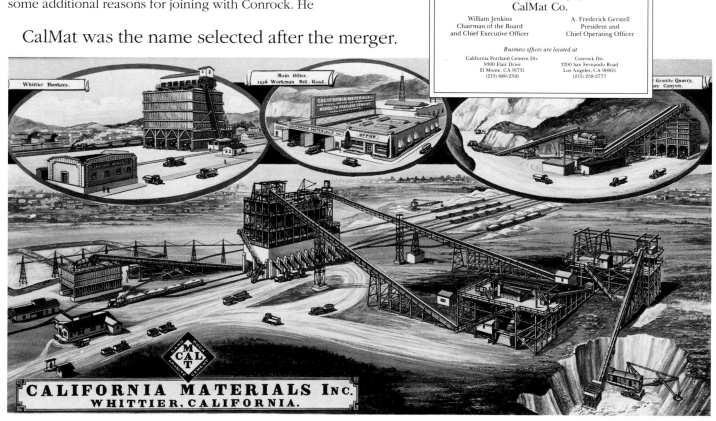

The "CALMAT" identification existed long before it became "CalMat."

available and the growth of the corporate interests.

Not only were family members on the Board and among the shareholders but the second and third generations of families were working in the plants.

Lengthy associations with the company and family ties were common in the plants — and this service was recognized. Wilson C. Hanna and Ernie Hendrickson had long terms at the Colton site and rose to the rank of Vice President, a title Hendrickson always felt had been granted at least partially in recognition of his long service.

Second, and in some cases third, generations continued to work for the company. Families could often easily reach beyond the half century mark in service when all the relatives were counted.

Terms on the Board of Directors tended to be lengthy also. Daniel Murphy, E.E. Duque, and L.E. Bancroft each served over thirty years. Richard Grant had been a director for over twenty years as had Asa Call, whose two terms spanned more than two decades.

California Portland Cement Company was a family enterprise in many ways. Although the directors represented all the shareholders, from 1904 to 1970, they tended to be related to the Flemings and Murphys or have a direct relationship to the daily management of the company. Archie McCall was perhaps the most notable example of this, having spent several decades with the company and serving as Executive Vice President before retiring and joining the Board.

Richard A. Grant, who married Mr. Fleming's granddaughter, had served on the Board of Directors since 1945 and was elected president in 1959. While this was a personnel change, it did not represent a change in the breadth of contacts maintained by members of the Board. Directors had long maintained contacts with the oil, banking and transportation industries.

During his tenure on the CPC Board, Grant also was a director of the Newhall Land and Farming, Security Pacific National Bank, Harvey Mudd College, the Santa

Families could easily reach beyond the half century mark.

*Ernie Hendrickson rose
from mule tender to Vice President*

Catalina Foundation and the Southern Pacific Company among others.

It was typical for the directors to be involved with a number of other companies and organizations. Asa Call, for example, was Chairman of Pacific Mutual Life Insurance Company, California's oldest life insurance company, and had served not only on the CPC board, but also those of Standard Oil Company and the Southern California Edison

*Richard A. Grant Sr., E.E. Duque, L.E. Bancroft and Archie McCall represent over
one hundred fifty years of service to California Portland Cement.*

Directors Encouraged the Family Association.

Michael A. Morphy was elected Chairman of the Board and Chief Executive Officer in 1981.

Company. Directors also, at various times, held positions on the governing board of the Automobile Club of Southern California.

The Directors had encouraged the family association throughout the organization by making frequent visits to the plants and talking with the staff. The fact that technology had made it possible to operate a cement plant with far fewer than the peak numbers of the 1920's made the

contact easier, although the establishment of the second and third location and the increasingly complex nature of conducting corporate business tended to make visits to a particular plant less frequent.

Nevertheless, employees, especially those who had been on the payroll for some time remembered the visits. A bond developed between employer and employee — a family bond.

It was a family which, for the most part, got along very well. The first strike in the company's history took place in 1981, when the international union struck all 10 cement plants in Southern California and Arizona.

The CPC family feeling had been anchored in the business approach of the Flemings and Duques who had made frequent visits to the plant at Colton and knew many of the employees on a first name basis. This familiarity was made easier by the fact that many of the employees worked many years for the company, it was common to promote from within the ranks, and the total number of workers was not large. A similar feeling of family existed within the Conrock organization.

Corporations, which are in reality paper entities, are much more easily merged and manipulated than families, which are composed of people. Within a short time it became evident that the California Portland and Conrock families were different organizations with rather different approaches to business life.

California Portland directors had come from the gentleman business class since the turn of the century. These were people who were interested in managing a profitable business, but who understood that the cement business, by its very nature, was not likely to return large profits every year.

They could boast of continually paying dividends for over 70 years, but the amounts had, at times, been relatively small. They were comfortable with a rather conservative business approach. Corporate letterhead, for example, bore Thomas J. Fleming's name as Secretary and

CPC's Board of Directors: Harry Conger, Archie McCall, Richard Grant Jr., A.F. Gerstell, Michael Morphy, Gordon Crary, Stuart Peeler, Thomas Lowe, and Thomas Call visited the Colton Plant in April, 1983.

Evans' task was to create a new corporation.

General Manager for several years after he died. It was simply crossed out and E.E. Duque's name typed over the top. It was evidently not thought necessary to obtain letterhead with the names of the new officers printed on it.

The company found it necessary to include an explanatory note with an annual report in the late 1960's which featured artwork on the cover, rather than the plain covers with the company logo which was the standard approach to annual reports both prior to and after the more lively version was published.

It was a financially conservative company which often looked to its own resources for capital expenditures. Although an 1895 Board resolution had authorized borrowing "for the best interest of the Company," this was not an authorization which, through the years, had been taken lightly.

Real estate tended to be carried on the company books at a value viewed in terms of its use to the cement producing segment of the company, not the more liberal potential market value. A shrewd Wall Street analyst might well see this as undervaluing the property. They would also undoubtedly notice the company's debt had been kept to a minimum.

While Conrock had established itself in the sand and gravel — and later ready mix — field partially through the acquisition of the property it worked, it too may have been viewed as undervaluing its assets. It did not share some of the other philosophies which had been long established at California Portland. With less investment in each of its sites, the bottom line on the balance sheet tended to be more important and the time was "now" — not somewhere in the future. There was not the same sense of need for connections within the social/business community which had been evident at California Portland's corporate level for many years.

It is difficult to take two relatively small families, merge them into a large group and still keep the sense of family that existed for either before they were joined together.

For California Portland Cement, much of the family feeling disappeared with the realization that, as a result of the merger with Conrock, it was now the cement division of CalMat, the new corporate entity, and had no corporate identity of its own.

Any consolidation of two organizations would naturally be expected to bring about the elimination of some overlapping administrative functions. To the cement people it seemed as though this was regularly done at the expense of staff with whom they had worked under the old independent format.

These changes were especially perplexing to CPC employees in light of the fact that California Portland had owned a 30% share in Consolidated Rock, the predecessor to Conrock, since the 1930's. Some had fully expected the CPC management team to displace that of Conrock.

Assets which had been the sole property of California Portland Cement were now the assets of the entire corporation and were, in some cases, viewed as saleable in the interest of reducing overall corporate debt. Funding for improvements tended to likewise be viewed in a broader scope than previously and the Cement Division at times found itself standing toward the rear of the allocation line.

Although the companies had strengthened their base with the merger, it did not ward off take over attempts. In 1987 Australian financier Ronald Brierley began his attempt to take over CalMat, the corporation formed with the merger of California Portland Cement and Conrock Company.

Seeking to avoid a hostile takeover, the young company looked for possible allies. It found one in the Onoda Cement Company which was willing to negotiate for the cement production facilities which had been California Portland Cement and 13 ready mix facilities which were to become Catalina Pacific Concrete Company.

Ron Evans, whose history with California Portland dated back more than twenty years and who had been assigned the task of explaining the controls in the modernized Colton plant, was selected to head the transition from CalMat back to California Portland. He had served as Executive Vice President and General Manager of the California Portland Cement Division.

Evans' task, which provided a challenge equal to the one he faced two decades earlier, was to create a new corporation within the course of the two year transition period decided upon by CalMat and Onoda. Working with the Onoda people, it was his responsibility to create a

CPC's management team takes a break from its meeting in Tucson. Left to right, back row: W.B. Jager, A.F. Gerstell, R.P. Strub, G.B. Crary, T.F. Call, A.L. McCall, M.Whitley, T.L. Lowe, M.A. Morphy. Front row: V. Corley, R.E. Evans, D. Cahn, T. Sarris, D. Collins.

Many of the advantages . . . were now realized.

ONODA CALIFORNIA, INC.

TELEPHONE
(818) 852-6200

2025 E. FINANCIAL WAY
GLENDORA, CA 91740 U.S.A.

FACSIMILE
(818) 963-7377

CALIFORNIA PORTLAND CEMENT COMPANY

P.O. BOX 910, MOJAVE, CALIFORNIA 93502 / TEL. (805) 824-2401 FAX (805) 824-4908

new organization from the ground up.

Some officers such as Skip Corley, Don Collins, John Frogge, Dave Cahn, and Bob Lamp who had been with California Portland previous to the merger, returned with the new company format. Others had to be recruited from outside the merged company.

It was a difficult task but one which was accomplished within the allotted time frame. California Portland Cement, with a century of history in cement production, was now a part of Onoda Cement, with an even longer history in the same field, having been established in 1881.

Many of the advantages which the company had sought with the CalMat merger were now realized. It was a private company and therefore not subject to take over wars. Furthermore, the company had returned to its major function. It was, once again, largely a producer of cement, but this with a delivery capacity in Catalina Pacific Concrete and with the financial backing of a company which was heavily involved with the modern production of cement.

Ron Evans joined CPC in 1961 and became President in 1990.

Onoda Cement Company and California Portland Cement Company share long histories in the cement business.

Left to right, front row: Jim Hurt, Phil Seki, Kazusuke Imamura, Kiyoshi Kusakabe, Ron Evans, Toro Inoue.
Center row: Ken Suzuki, Isao Yamane, Shigeji Yagi, Tommy Kimura, V. Corley, Danny Ichikawa.
Back row: Don Collins, Bob Lamp, Jim Wendoll, Dave Cahn.

Sites / Geology

LONG BEFORE THERE WERE MEN TESTING THEIR SKILLS AND ABILITIES IN AN EFFORT TO MAKE CEMENT, THERE WERE THE MOUNTAINS. They were mountains in three locations, separated by hundreds of miles, within what was to become a primary marketing area larger than many states.

Cement workers and marketing areas are very much a latter day concept. The mountains in Colton, Rillito and Mojave were formed hundreds of millions of years ago, long before the first record of people encroaching on their territory.

They had in common a single chemical combination which produced the major ingredient in making cement — limestone. Three different locations, brought together only by their natural mineral content and the artificial acquisitions of men.

While each of the mountains shares some common history, there are some differences. These differences are most notable in the individual geological formations. The changes that occurred , both geological and man-made, are obvious and fascinating.

Up-grading and modernizing cement production helped change the sites and influenced the economy of the three locations. Site selection was based upon not only the rich limestone deposits but also potential markets and accessible transportation. The long-term development of these site decisions helped shape the company as well as the market it served.

Chapter Three

SLOVER-A UNIQUE FORMATION
COLTON

". . . Hill of the Ravens."

Mt. Slover, as the deposit at Colton was to be called, was a unique formation. It has been described as a "block fault, four way formation," It differs from other extrusive masses. It is a block line, square body instead of one created by some giant crack or break in the earth's surface.

At one point the area which was to become Slover Mountain lay beneath the sea where layered beds of limestone and shale were deposited. The layers metamorphosed or changed into marble and schist as a result of the pressure upon the layers due to the depth of their burial.

Next came the intrusion of the granitic rock. This took place on the north end of the deposit and tilted the layers up to the extent that they slanted southeast at a 45 to 50 degree angle. This tilting caused the limestone and shale to break apart in large blocks, leaving space between the blocks.

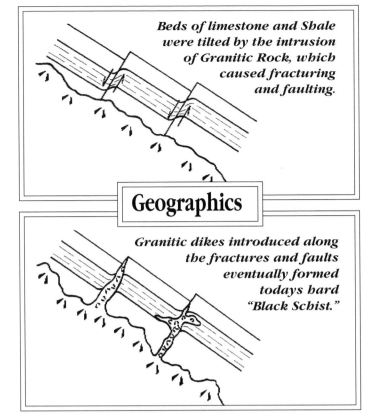

Beds of limestone and Shale were tilted by the intrusion of Granitic Rock, which caused fracturing and faulting.

Geographics

Granitic dikes introduced along the fractures and faults eventually formed todays hard "Black Schist."

Mt. Slover stands alone rising 500 feet above the neighboring landscape.

Cerrito Solo, the little hill that stands alone, stood beside the road to Mission San Gabriel.

Later, more granitic material intruded into the available spaces, which created the hard "Black Schist" through heat and chemical action. During the course of time erosion took place, cutting down the area around what was to become Mt. Slover. The formation was left as a mountain with its peak approximately 1500 feet above sea level and 500 feet above the surrounding country side.

To the Indians, who may have come to the area south of Mt. Slover by 2000 B.C., it was known as the Hill of the Ravens. While there is evidence of the presence of the Indians in the area around the mountain it seems to have been only temporary. Permanent settlements do not seem to have existed.

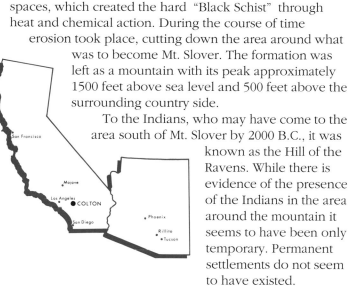

GROWTH / CHANGE

GEOLOGY	Sediment layers of limestone & shale deposited
	Marble and schist formed
	Layers tilted by intrusion of Granitic Rock
	Fracturing and faulting takes place
	Granitic dikes intrude along fractures and faults
2000-1000 B.C.	Indians establish temporary settlements in Mt. Slover area
1827	Asistencia established as adjunct to Mission San Gabriel
1840's	Isaac Slover settles near Mountain
1870's	Marble & limestone quarry operations begins
1873	Slover Mountain Colony Association founded
1875	Town of Colton founded
	Southern Pacific Railroad line reaches Colton
1887	City of Colton incorporated
1892	Construction begins on CPCC's Mill A

In 1905 Mill A shown with the steep N.W. face of Slover Mt. The fault face is the uptilted end of Slover limestone block.

Spaniards named the mountain Cerrito Solo, the little hill that stands alone, for it seemed neither part of nor as high as the mountains which rise above neighboring San Bernardino. During the period of Spanish rule a series of missions was established in California.

While the missions themselves were near the coast, the land under their jurisdiction could extend inland for quite some distance. San Bernardino Valley, in which Mt. Slover is located, came under the control of Mission San Gabriel. In 1827 an asistencia was established at the old Indian rancheria of Guachama. Travelers along the road between the mission at San Gabriel and asistencia passed by Mt. Slover. Some have conjectured that the lime used as either mortar or white wash at the asistencia came from the mountain.

Isaac Slover, the first known American settler in the San Bernardino Valley, lived at the base of the mountain

The QUARRY. . .

Early quarry work on Mt. Slover.

Early construction scenes. . .

above – Early quarry work was labor intensive. Mule carts were used to carry the rock from the quarry.

left – Construction of number four stockhouse — 1916.

below left – Construction of the new store and shop buildings shown in 1926 .

below right – Construction of number five stockhouse — c.1920 –23.

Colton Cement was shipped throughout the world.

during the period of Spanish and Mexican government in California. It is from him that the mountain of minerals gained the name by which it has been known for over a century.

The mountain in turn, gave its name to the Slover Mountain Colony Association which was founded in 1873 and became the basis for the city of Colton. Colton was established as a town along the Southern Pacific Railroad line in 1875 and incorporated as a city twelve years later.

The city gave its name to the Cement manufactured at Mt. Slover and shipped throughout the world.

California Portland Cement Company began producing

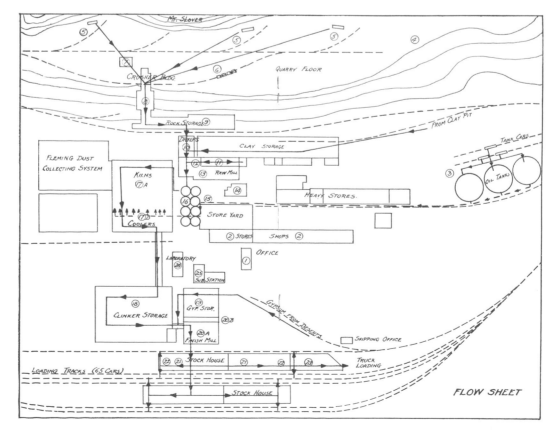

Plant guide/information booklet — prior to modernization.

Fifty years of cement production has left its mark on the mountain.

Mt. Slover 1953

Colton Cement in 1894, using a quarry on the north side of Mt. Slover, about 150 feet below the peak. The limestone was blasted from the side of the mountain, broken into pieces small enough to be placed in quarry carts drawn by burros, and transported to a crusher located above Mill A. After the initial crushing, the rock was sent by gravity down a 370 foot long wooden chute to a second, finer, crusher at the mill. This chute was lined with metal and constructed at a 30 degree incline. It became an easily recognized feature of Mill A.

California Portland was not the first company to quarry rock from Mt. Slover. Several had quarried and cut lime-

stone and marble from the mountain as early as the 1870's. In 1887 the Colton Marble and Lime Company operated on the south east side of the mountain with one of its two quarries just north of the plant where the stone was cut.

With the completion of Mill B, in 1907 California Portland Cement moved the major portion of its cement operation to the south side of the mountain. While Mill A had been built on the slope of the mountain side, Mill B was constructed below the floor level of the quarry. This provided for better use of the force of gravity and the movement of raw material from the quarry to the processing site.

Subsequent plants were built in approximately the same location and the rock, which had originally been loaded on carts drawn by burros and later by mules, was finally loaded into trucks and carried to a primary crusher.

The trucks grew larger and more efficient over the years and at one time featured a unique side dump configuration. This allowed them to simply drive by the side of the crusher and dump the rock load from the quarry.

Blasting the rock from the quarry has changed significantly through the years also. It is no longer as much a ceremonial functional action, as it was when the company president would come to the quarry and throw the switch to activate the blast charges. The resulting blast could produce as much as a full years supply of rock. Today's effort is much more scientific as the plant seeks the right combination of rock and additives to make Colton Cement.

Mt. Slover 1926

Mt. Slover 1976

ARIZONA'S TWIN PEAKS
RILLITO

"Three different limestones. . . "

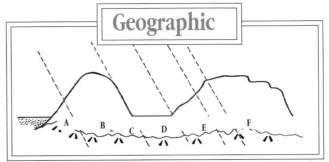

Geographic

Layers of A-Pinal schist, B-Bolsa quartzite, C-Abrigo shale, D-Martin limestone, E-Escabrosa limestone, and F- Naco limestone were tilted and eroded.

Arizona's Twin Peaks provide the source of limestone for the Arizona Portland Cement Company. Located 18 miles northwest of the modern city of Tucson, they include rock which was formed more than 600 million years ago. Today they stand as a west, the smaller of the two, and east hill.

The east hill consists of quartzites, shales, schists and limestones. Its sister to the west contains quartzite and schist. Flat beds of minerals were pushed upward by the intrusion of granite. The beds were tilted up on end until the formation reached a angle of about 65 degrees.

Three different limestones are quarried at the Rillito facility - Naco, Escabrosa and Martin. All are in the deposit which was pushed and tilted to form the east hill of Twin Peaks.

They each have their peculiar characteristic. Naco is high siliceous limestone, Escabrosa is high grade calcitic limestone and Martin usually is characterized by a high magnesium content. It is understandable that these quite different limestone deposits require blending before they are converted into a uniform cement.

When the company first began working these deposits, there was a long ridge extending approximately 2000 feet from the east hill. Mining the minerals has changed this from a ridge to a pit, the floor of which is nearly 200 feet below the surrounding land surface.

Limestone layers in the northern portion of the quarry were subject to folding under pressure and ultimately broke at their crests. Movement continued, forcing the upper segment of the fold up and over the lower portion. This produced limestone deposits quite different from those found in Colton, where the layers had not been subjected to folding and retained the characteristics of large blocks

The quarry road interrupts the tree line before it crosses the desert expanse to the "twin peaks."

Santa Cruz Valley settlement began in the 17th Century.

being tilted on their ends.

The "twins" witnessed the coming of the Indians, the exploration and settlement of the Spaniards and the subsequent conflicts, which were to continue as citizens of the United States pushed ever farther Westward.

Spanish exploration of the Santa Cruz Valley dates from 1539, with actual settlement beginning about 1691. The renowned Father Kino established settlements on the Santa Cruz River. Spanish control of the area followed the usual pattern of missions, pueblos and forts.

In 1776 Tucson was established as a Spanish fort to provide protection from the Indians, who were much more hostile than those found in California. The mission San Xavier del Bac was built about nine miles south of Tucson.

Unlike California and much of the

GROWTH / CHANGE

GEOLOGY	Sedimentary layers of limestone and shale deposited
	Layers deformed by folding and faulting surface erosion takes place
1539	Friar Marcos de Niza comes to Santa Cruz Valley
1691	Father Kino establishes settlements along the Santa Cruz River
1776	Tucson becomes Spanish fort
1846-48	Mexican War
1853	Gadsden Purchase
1863	Arizona Territory established
1912	Arizona becomes a state
1923	California Portland acquires the limestone deposit near Rillito
1948	Plant construction begins

Nearly a decade of change is evidenced in this view of the plant location near the Santa Cruz River.

Work began on the kiln, crusher, and conveyor.

Modernization in the early 1970's brought a new kiln, with preheater tower (top, left and right), a 3,000 H.P. raw mill (bottom left), and the covered conveyor belt from the quarry (bottom right) to the plant.

rest of Arizona, this territory did not become part of the United States as a result of the Mexican War in 1846. It was obtained as part of the Gadsden Purchase in 1853.

The twin peaks maintained a silent vigil over the landscape as human struggles went on around them and the forces of erosion worked on their surface. Although the men of California Portland Cement Company had been interested in an Arizona operation as early as the 1920's— and the original agreement with Dr. George Duryee had

included Arizona — it was not until the late 1940's that CPC men met this mountain with the full force of their knowledge, experience and, in some cases, equipment sent from the Colton facility.

Even then the forces of nature had to be taken into consideration. The cement plant was located about five miles from the deposit, due to the unpredictable nature of the Santa Cruz River. It would have been less expensive to locate the plant adjacent to the deposit, as had been done at

Over four decades of progress...

Mt. Slover, but it would also have required taking a chance that you would be cut off from the rest of the world, if the river washed out the access road.

Modernization and expansion of the plant between 1970 and 1972 included the installation of a covered conveyor belt 30" wide and just under four miles long, which took the rock from a crusher at the quarry along the side of the road and into the plant. Nature, however, finally played a cruel trick on the company planners. Rather than destroying the road from the quarry to the plant, it flooded the plant itself in 1978!

Over forty years passed between the time two CPC employees inspected the Rillito site in 1934 (below left) and the completion of APC's precalciner on No.4 kiln (right). In the intervening years the plant changed from a single stack reaching into the sky in 1949 to today's modern cement facility.

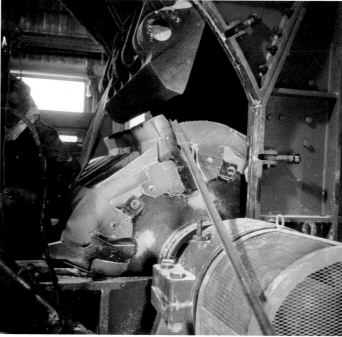

The noise of the primary impact crusher provides a marked contrast to the tranquility of the cotton fields at Rillito.

ONCE A SHALLOW SEA
MOJAVE

"It pushed into the limestone. . . "

Today's hot, arid and windy desert landscape was once, perhaps during the middle or late Paleozoic period in geologic time, a shallow sea. Flat layers of limestone, shale, and, to a minor extent, sandstone were deposited in this sea.

As had been the case at Colton and Rillito, the relative symmetry of these layers was altered by a granitic intrusion pushing up from below the deposits. This intrusion uplifted the deposits, but did not result in the layers being tilted and broken as the layers at Colton.

At the Mojave site the intrusion of granitic rock took place approximately 70 to 140 million years ago. It pushed into the limestone, shale, and quartzite layers, forming hills and valleys. The "hills" were capped with the materials which had formed the original layers. These are called roof pendants.

During the course of time, erosion worked on the deposit, generally leaving the "hills", topped with the roof pendants of mineral deposits, higher than the valleys.

Layers of limestone, shale and quartzite were pushed upward by intrusions of Granitic Rock, forming caps known as roof pendants.

Geographics

Erosion later took place and the Garlock Fault contributed to folding of the rocks in the northern part of the modern quarry.

Southern Pacific's branch line to Creal was part of the initial development of the Mojave plant.

Creal is the official name for the site.

Additional change in the formation took place due to the proximity of the deposits to the Garlock Fault. This earthquake fault was responsible for the severe folding of the rocks in the northern part of the Mojave Quarry. The portion of the layers closest to the fault had a tendency to move or drag along the fault line. The portions farther from the fault tended to be more stable.

Creal is the official name for the cement plant location in the southeastern portion of Kern County. Named for Wilson Creal Hanna, one of the longest term employees and a vice president of California Portland Cement Company, it is a stop on a branch line of the Southern Pacific Railroad.

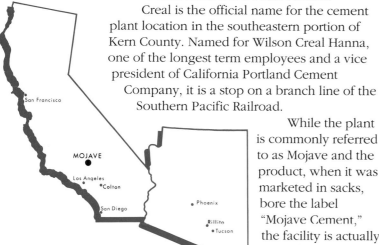

While the plant is commonly referred to as Mojave and the product, when it was marketed in sacks, bore the label "Mojave Cement," the facility is actually several miles from the town, with access from Oak

GROWTH / CHANGE

Geology	Layers of limestone, shale, and sandstone deposited in shallow sea
	Granitic intrusion lifts deposited layers and forms roof pendants
	Erosion creates hills and valleys
1776	Father Graces travels through Mojave area
1876	Mojave established as a town
	Southern Pacific Railroad extended to Mojave
1884	Twenty mule team borax wagon trains arrive
1905	Los Angeles Aqueduct construction
1952	Limestone deposits purchased by CPC
	Tehachapi/Bakersfield earthquake
1955	Railroad branch to Creal completed

Early construction at Mojave was a continuous process.

*The geodesic dome became a distinctive part of the
Mojave plant during the MOMOD Project.*

*Wind generators border the plant property
to the north and west .*

Creek Road. It is not far from some of the 4,000
machines which are used in the wind farms of the
area to produce alternative energy.

The town of Mojave is located in the high
desert. With the elevation of over 2500 feet, it lies in
the foothills of the Sierra Nevada range. The settlement was named for the desert area immediately to
the east which, in turn, was named for the river that
runs through the area. The river was named for the
Mojave Indians who occupied the desert area and
were one of the few California Indian groups to
engage in trading with tribes beyond those in the
immediate vicinity.

The first white men to enter
into the Mojave area were Spaniards
and one of the earliest travelers was
Father Francisco Graces who
arrived in 1776, probably stopping
at nearby Willow Springs and
passing through Oak Creek Pass.

Father Graces had begun his
journey early in March 1776,
starting at the Gila River walking to
Mission San Gabriel. It was on his
return trek that he passed by the
area of present day Mojave. He
continued beyond the Gila River
starting point and returned to
Mission San Xavier Del Bac near
Tucson having walked 2700 miles.

Mojave has a long association with transportation and mining endeavors. Started as a railroad town when the Southern Pacific was pushing into the desert country in 1876, it served as the railhead for wagon freight in the area.

The most notable freight came from the borax at the Searles Lake, about 80 miles away and at Death Valley. The now famous 20 mule teams bringing borax over 160 miles from Death Valley were common sites in the Mojave area between 1884 and 1888.

Late in the 19th Century gold was discovered in the area and gold mining experienced a revival in the 1930's. Beginning in the late 1960's, the tailings from some of this mining activity were used at the Mojave plant.

In the early years of the twentieth Century, Mojave experienced a boom as a result of the construction on the Los Angeles Aqueduct, which brought water from the Owens Valley to Los Angeles.

Throughout the boom periods and between them, Mojave continued to serve as a transportation center. It remains the transportation hub for eastern Kern County boasting of both major highway and railroad routes.

Production capacity nearly doubled with the addition of the precalciner kiln to the existing kilns.

PRODUCT

THE ROMANS HAD A WORD FOR IT - *CAEMENTUM*, MEANING TO CUT DOWN IN SIZE. This had evolved from the early use of a mortar made from the fragments cut from stones used in the construction of such structures as the pyramids. Evolution of the term after the Roman times eventually brought forth today's "cement."

It is somewhat ironic that the word which originated with the concept of cutting is used today most frequently with the concept of bringing together. We talk of cementing relationships and friendships.

Cement is the bonding agent. It is also the major ingredient in concrete. While we may cement relationships, we recognize the permanence of concrete when we talk of principles or positions which are "set in concrete."

Cement and concrete are the major products of *California Portland Cement Company*. They are both the oldest product, cement having first been produced in 1894, and the newest product, concrete having become a direct company product with the formation of Catalina Pacific Corporation shortly before the company's centennial year.

California Portland had been involved in other products, the most important of which was lime, but cement remained the major focus of the business. Some diversification took place with the acquisition of a coal mine and an oil exploration firm.

The coal, however, was largely seen as a source of fuel for the cement plants and the oil company was always referred to in the annual reports as a speculative venture. The same could be said for ventures into the field of environmental concerns, roofing products, and building products.

Throughout the first 100 years of its existence, California Portland has concentrated on manufacturing cement for use in concrete and nearly all of the other ventures undertaken by the company had some relationship to that central product.

Chapter Four

POWDERED ROCK- CRUSHED
CEMENT

"...chemists held the key."

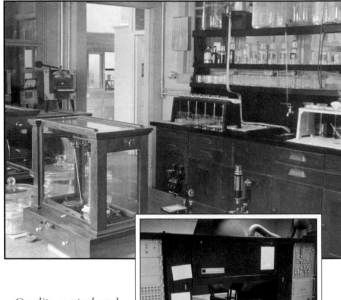

Quality control and analysis has always been an important part of the production process.

Making portland cement has been described as crushing a mountain and putting it through a sieve. There is some validity to this description, but it tends to place too much emphasis on the mechanics of the process. If that was the most important element, engineers would be the key to successful cement operations.

In reality, chemists have held the key. Powdered rock, no matter how finely crushed, does not automatically turn into portland cement. It requires a chemical reaction between the various raw materials and that takes place in the presence of intense heat.

The blend of ingredients used in the cement making process and the length of time required to heat these ingredients to the ideal temperature is something left to the chemists. Today's chemist can rely on a wide range of monitoring and controlling devices to assist in getting just the right combination of elements into the kilns. Once in the kiln, the correct temperature must be maintained for a specific period of time.

On the surface this process seems fairly simple. It requires a limited number of basic ingredients and a standard process which has not fundamentally changed since California Portland Cement first began production in 1894.

The basic raw materials can still be divided into those which supply the lime component (calcareous), the silica component (siliceous), the alumina component (argilla-ceous) and the iron component (ferriferous). The secret is knowing the correct proportions.

These proportions will vary with the types of raw materials used. While limestone is the common source of the lime component in Southern California, there are a number of other possible sources of lime, including chalk and oyster shells. Limestone is the most convenient and practical for cement plants operating in this area. Choices exist for the other components as well and will vary with available ingredients.

The "recipe" is complicated by the fact that few, if any, of the ingredients are 100% pure. They are natural rather than manufactured components and subject to some impurities. Furthermore, the impurities are not consistent throughout. Limestone in the deposit at Rillito, for example, is not the same in all parts of the deposit. Impurities must be identified and taken into consideration. Adjustments have to be made.

One method of making these adjustments is to analyze the limestone at the quarry before the rock is removed. This allows for selective quarry operations.

Analysis and control are the watchwords in making portland cement. Knowing the composition of the raw materials and controlling the mixture of raw materials and additives is essential to the production of a uniform product.

Analysis begins with systematic series of core drillings in the quarry to determine the exact location of various rock formations. Daily quarry operations are then planned, taking into consideration the proportions of shale, lime-stone, and other rock formations.

Once the analysis has been completed, the

It takes 1.56 tons of raw material to produce a ton of cement.

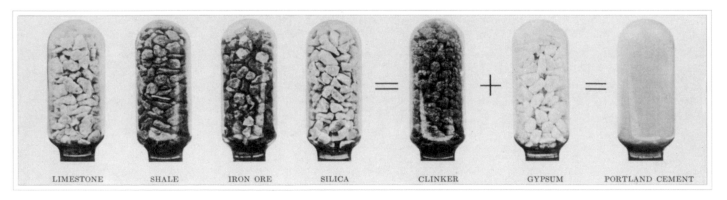

| LIMESTONE | SHALE | IRON ORE | SILICA | CLINKER | GYPSUM | PORTLAND CEMENT |

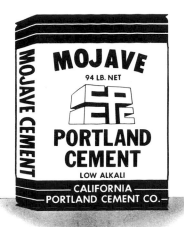

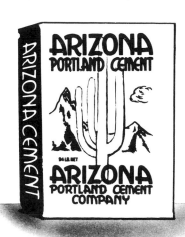

DATE_____

PURCHASER_____

STREET ADDRESS_____

TOWN_____

BOUGHT OF
CALIFORNIA PORTLAND CEMENT CO.
601 WEST FIFTH STREET -:- LOS ANGELES

QUANTITY_____BARRELS COLTON PORTLAND

CEMENT, TO BE USED IN THE CONSTRUCTION OF_____

_____

_____

GROSS, PER BARREL—IN CLOTH SACKS ..... $_____

GROSS, PER BARREL—IN PAPER SACKS ..... $_____

DELIVERY: F. O. B._____

SACK RETURNS: A credit of 10-cents each (40¢ per barrel) will be allowed on empty cloth sacks of our brand returned to us in serviceable condition. No return allowance on paper sacks.

CASH DISCOUNT: A cash discount of 20¢ per barrel will be allowed on invoices paid in full on or before 10th of month following date of shipment.

_____PURCHASER
ACCEPTED:
CALIFORNIA PORTLAND CEMENT COMPANY

BY_____

FORM 259—1M—50559

California Portland Cement Co.

CLINKER SHEET

NO. OF CARS	Kiln No. 1	Kiln No. 2	Kiln No. 3	Kiln No. 4	Kiln No. 5
1	4852	4992	4616	4474	4618
2	4874	4882	4692	5112	4912
3	5058	5034	4650	4888	4714
4	4772	4844	4894	5000	4912
5	4862	4600	4924	5000	4920
6	5252	4822	4802	4792	4752
7	5218	4790	4952	4780	4702
8	4966	4680	5100	5062	4526
9	5000	4804	4842	4974	4402
10	4962	4784	4858	4852	4702
11	4958	5056	4920	4806	4712
12	4940	4754	4704	4562	4856
13	4922	4712	4816	5084	4776
14	4910	4572	4760	5024	4650
15	4886	4750	4842	4830	
16	4812	4596	4552	4598	66184
17	4880	4604	4662	4722	18718
18	4692	8216	4808	4602	47466
19	88406	22729	4640		87162
20	24066	58487	90934	24066	
21	64340		25403	63096	
22			65531		9

Kiln 1 ____ Bbls.   Total No. Cars ____   48
     2 ____   Average per Car ____ Bbls.   30
     3 ____   87
     4 ____
     5 ____
Total ____

---

limestone can be blasted from the face of the quarry and transported to a crusher. Gyratory, jaw and roll crushers are just three of several approaches to the job of reducing oversize boulders, which may weigh up to 18,000 pounds, to large rocks.

The large rocks may go to hammer or impact mills where they are further reduced in size. Along the way the rock passes through sampling stations and automatic scales which provide information on tonnage and chemical composition.

This information is used to determine which materials should be added from segregated rock storage bins. The "raw mix" is further blended and adjusted before it travels to a roller or ball mill for initial grinding.

One might describe the ball mill as something which converts pebbles to powder. Forged grinding balls from one to four inches in diameter rotate within a large cylinder to pulverize the raw mix. Steel ridges inside the cylinder carry the balls half way through a rotation and drop them down on the raw mix. The result is a material about 1/1300" in size which is sent to the homogenizing silos where it is thoroughly mixed and blended.

To this point the reduction, blending and homogenizing has been a physical process. It is followed by a chemical transformation which takes place in the kiln, which is heated to nearly 3000 degrees Fahrenheit.

Heating the mixture is a key factor and, in the process of becoming more energy efficient, preheaters and precalciners have been employed. These towers use the hot gases produced by the kiln to heat the raw mix before it enters the kiln, thereby reducing the amount of time needed in the kilns.

Kilns are huge rotating cylinders lined with fire brick and installed on a slight decline which allows the natural flow of raw mix from the feed (upper) end to the burning zone. The raw mix is subjected to intense heat and becomes partially liquefied.

In the process carbon dioxide gases are released, molecular restructuring takes place and solid calcium silicates are produced, along with the liquid. The silicates are responsible for the strength produced on hydration of the cement.

When the mix enters the relatively cooler tempera-

From quarry to customer...

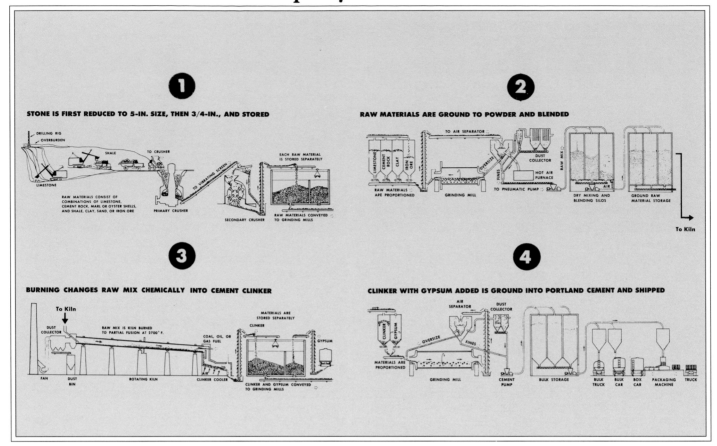

❶ STONE IS FIRST REDUCED TO 5-IN. SIZE, THEN 3/4-IN., AND STORED

❷ RAW MATERIALS ARE GROUND TO POWDER AND BLENDED

❸ BURNING CHANGES RAW MIX CHEMICALLY INTO CEMENT CLINKER

❹ CLINKER WITH GYPSUM ADDED IS GROUND INTO PORTLAND CEMENT AND SHIPPED

tures at the discharge end of the kiln, the liquid solidifies to form aluminate and iron compounds. These are largely responsible for the rate of setting during hydration.

The solidified material which emerges from the kiln is referred to as clinker and is even harder than the rock from which it was produced, although it was much more brittle. Once the clinker has been cooled and passed through a chunk breaker, it is conveyed to storage.

One final mixing takes place when the clinker goes to the finish mill for grinding and gypsum is added. It is the gypsum which regulates the setting time of the cement in concrete. Huge ball mills pulverize the clinker and gypsum to a powder so fine it will pass through a sieve having 100,000 squares to the inch.

After the finish grinding, the powder goes to storage silos. Later it may be blown into self closing sacks or held for bulk transport in trucks or rail cars.

The process described rather briefly to this point results in a product known as portland cement. This is a specific type of cement, but one so common today that it has almost become a generic designation. When one speaks of cement, it is implied that the product is portland cement.

The term "Portland Cement" was patented in 1824 by Joseph Aspdin of England, although it is clear that John Smeaton made the connection between a hydraulic cement and the popular Portland Stone used in building over sixty years earlier.

Smeaton had been commissioned to rebuild the Eddystone Lighthouse and was naturally interested in a cement which would adhere well despite the best efforts of the storms off the coast of Cornwell, England. Through experimentation he discovered limestone with a considerable amount of clay served his purpose much better than that which was purer or harder.

Cement, in some form, dates from at least the period of the pharaohs when the Egyptians used impure gypsum plaster as mortar in pyramid construction. Cement is a binding agent and the term derives from a Latin verb meaning "to cut". This originally referred to the stone cuttings used in lime mortar. The Egyptians had learned to burn the chips which accumulated when the blocks of stone they were cutting were trimmed. They made a mortar from the chips.

Both the Greeks and Romans used a pozzolanic mortar formed by mixing finely ground volcanic material with lime, sand, and water. Pozzolana hardens by reacting chemically with the lime.

The Roman influence can be seen in the fact that the name is taken from the Italian town of Possuoli, where a suitable volcanic ingredient was found. Cements made with this volcanic ingredient were resistant if exposed to water. Pozzolanic cement was used in the Roman Coliseum and the Pantheon. It was also the cement shipped to Mojave for construction of that plant.

Long after the fall of Rome, John Smeaton was commissioned to rebuild the Eddystone Lighthouse near Cornwall, England. He knew of lime-pozzolana mortars and was aware they were not always satisfactory for underwater construction. He experimented a bit and discovered that better limes were those made from limestone containing a considerable amount of clay. Smeaton is credited with

Type III is high-early-strength cement. The British have a comparable cement which they call "rapid hardening".This product is used were concrete must be placed in service as soon as possible.

Type IV is low heat cement and used where considerable thicknesses of concrete are required and the rise in temperature might be excessive. This change in temperature could lead to excessive volume change and cracking. Type IV is usually produced only for special large projects.

Type V cement is for use where high sulfate resistance is required.

In addition to the above, there are some special portlands, which are cements modified by small additions of chemical agents to make them useful as oil well cement or more workable for use in stucco or exterior plaster. The latter are called plastic cements. California Portland developed a gun plastic cement which could be applied with a "gun" using air pressure.

There are also blends, which add in other materials such as the pozzolan mentioned previously. This produces a cement which has a lower rate of heat liberation than Type I.

Masonry cements, which California Portland has produced, are commonly made by fine grinding portland cement with limestone and an air-entraining

COLTON
"GUN PLASTIC"
will mean...
- greater efficiency
- maximum productivity
- superior quality work

This is THE product for use with a plastering machine!

being the first to recognize what constitutes a hydraulic lime.

In 1796, forty years after Smeaton's experimentation, James Parker, an Englishman, patented a hard-burned impure lime. He called it Roman cement and it gained wide usage. It is essentially a natural cement, which requires grinding, but is made with a lower firing temperature than portland cement and has hydraulic properties which are relatively low.

It was natural cement made from "cement rock' which had the major portion of the domestic market in the United States prior to the introduction of portland cement. This was the product with which California Portland Cement was competing during the early years of its existence.

Portland cement in the United States is really a phenomenon of the Twentieth Century when it came to dominate the cement industry and all but eliminate the production of natural cement. There are several types of portland cement, designated with Roman numerals I through V by the American Society for Testing and Materials.

Type I is intended for general concrete construction where no special properties are necessary.

Type II is used where concrete may be exposed to moderate sulfate action or where no more than moderate liberation of heat is advisable.

agent. The entrained air improves workability, and the limestone,though not cementitious, is considered desirable as a filler.

CEMENT AND WATER MIXTURE
C O N C R E T E

"Cement is the key ingredient. . ."

An old song extolling the virtues of love and marriage boldly stated, *"you can't have one without the other."* This is also true for cement and concrete. It just isn't the same until they are joined together.

Concrete consists of a mixture of portland cement and water brought together to bind inert aggregates into a rocklike mass. Cement is the key ingredient as it is the chemical reaction between the cement and the water which produces the hardened "paste" to bind everything together.

Concrete could be made with other cements, but is commonly made with portland cement. Portland cement became the dominant material used shortly after the turn of the century. It is, in fact, so commonly used in the mixture that unless otherwise specified, it is assumed to be the ingredient.

Sand, gravel, and crushed stone are the aggregates most often found in the concrete mixture, although other materials could be used. The type and weight of the aggregates will vary with the intended use of the concrete. A dense concrete mixture which might be used for shielding in atomic reactor structures could weigh as much as 250 pounds per cubic foot, whereas the more ordinary weight would be about 150 pounds per cubic foot. The higher density could be obtained through the use of heavier aggregates.

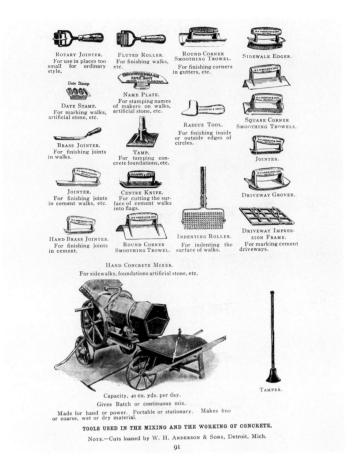

TOOLS USED IN THE MIXING AND THE WORKING OF CONCRETE.
Note.—Cuts loaned by W. H. Anderson & Sons, Detroit, Mich.
91

Compressive strength can also be varied. This is accomplished by changing the proportions in the concrete mixture.

Although it is common to think of concrete as something quite dense and heavy, it is possible to make the

Los Angeles Colosseum under construction

Reinforcing concrete increases structural versatility.

The Westin Bonaventure - Los Angeles

mixture so light using light aggregates or a special foaming process that the result will float on water. This light concrete, weighing as little as 30 pounds per cubic foot, can be sawed and nailed like wood.

Clearly the type of concrete used is related to the finished product desired. Usually this is will involve the construction of some structure such as a large building, a dam, or a highway. It could also be an irrigation project, airport runway or silo.

One of the most common uses for concrete is in the construction of streets, sidewalks, and curbs. Colton cement was used in the concrete which formed the basis for several of the streets in the town of Colton and in sidewalks and curbs as well. It has been used extensively in the streets and highways throughout Southern California and in buildings throughout the world..

Once the proportions are determined, mixing cement with the aggregates to form concrete is a fairly straight forward activity. In Southern California prior to the early 1930's this was a task which took place at the job site for major construction projects—and was subject to a great deal of inconsistency.

With the advent of the ready-mix trucks, concrete which was uniformly mixed and of much better quality could be delivered to construction sites. The result, of course, was a much better finished product.

The basic ingredients still had to be stored somewhere and this became the function of batch plants. It is at the batch plant that the concrete is mixed and loaded into the ready mix vehicles for transportation to the job site. Since

Los Angeles Swimming
Stadium 1932

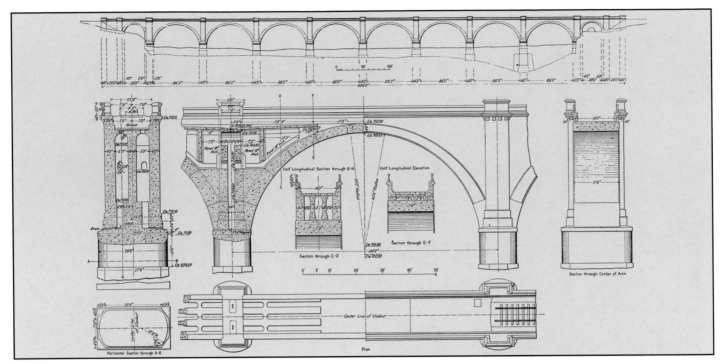

transportation can be a major factor in the delivered price of concrete, it is in a company's best interest to have several batch plants which are conveniently located throughout its market area.

Concrete by itself has some limitations as a building material. It can be made more versatile when combined with steel bars or mesh, thereby forming what is commonly known as reinforced concrete. The steel provides the reinforcement and increases the capability of sustaining heavy loads over wider spans of space.

The reinforcement concept works because steel and concrete have approximately equal coefficients of thermal expansion and the cement in the concrete bonds well with the steel, thereby transferring the concrete to the steel while protecting the steel from corrosion. The location of reinforcing steel bars is determined by the use of the concrete structure. Bridge girders which span the distance between two abutments will not have the same bar place-

"... quite different from the light, graceful structures..."

ment as concrete light poles or chimneys.

It is interesting to note the engineers who designed the railroad bridge over the Santa Ana River at Riverside in the early years of this century chose to use Colton Cement and a technique which did not employ reinforced concrete, although that option was available. The bridge remains in use today, supporting ever longer freight trains on a regular basis.

The railroad bridge is a massive structure, reminiscent of the ancient Roman Aqueducts, and quite different from some

Over half a century passed between the construction of Riverside's railroad bridge & San Diego's Convention Center.

light graceful structures we see today. Often these structures are made possible through the use of prestressed concrete, which allows longer free spans in bridges, lighter, and more graceful buildings, without the loss of strength.

Prestressed concrete has been described as "reinforced concrete which has been placed in a state of permanent precompression before service loads are applied." Essentially this is accomplished by applying tension to the steel rods or wire used in the reinforcement.

Precast structural concrete, which provides large sections of concrete already poured and dried, is used in conjunction with prestressed concrete in the building of decks for highway bridges, floor and roof slabs, wall panels and interior support elements. "Instant buildings" have become a feature of Southern California, as precast wall panels transform a structural skeleton into a building, seemingly overnight.

"Instant " buildings, of course, are an illusion, created by the fact that the walls are set in place quickly and provide a shell within which to continue work. Prior to the arrival of the shell, work must be completed on the foundation and the floor slab.

Concrete is brought to the site in ready mix trucks to fulfill

ARIZONA CAPITOL BUILDING.
California Portland Cement used in fireproof construction.

NORTH RIVERSIDE AND JARUPA CANAL COMPANY'S CANAL.
Fourteen miles plastered with California Portland Cement mortar

BROADWAY TUNNEL, CITY OF LOS ANGELES.
8000 barrels California Portland Cement used.   Burleigh & Edwards, Contractors

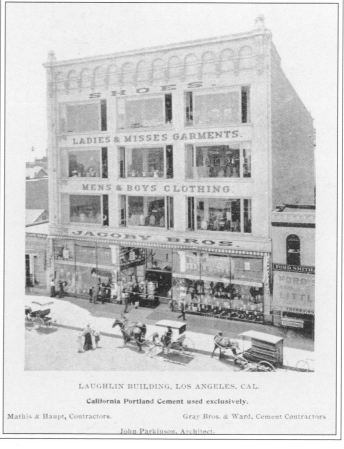

LAUGHLIN BUILDING, LOS ANGELES, CAL.
California Portland Cement used exclusively.
Mathis & Haupt, Contractors.   Gray Bros. & Ward, Cement Contractors
John Parkinson, Architect.

Batch plants serve as "delivery depots"

these needs and others, which can't be met by the use of precast concrete. Catalina Pacific trucks can be found at sites throughout their marketing area. Batch plants, like cement plants, have remained fundamentally the same through the years. What they do has not changed nearly as much as how they do it. The basic ingredients for concrete have not changed dramatically.

Delivery systems have changed. Ready mix trucks have long since replaced the dump trucks which delivered raw materials prior to the 1930's. The raw materials are now "delivered" to the ready mix truck at the batch plant. They are carefully weighed and mixed at the plant to provide the appropriate concrete for each job.

Many of those jobs have been streets and highways. These have proven to be something of a "self-help" project for the industry. The ready mix trucks provided concrete to build better transportation routes which, in turn, could support larger trucks. This allowed the ready mix trucks to increase in size and efficiency. Without a substantial road network, the heavily loaded ready mix trucks would not be able to reach construction sites.

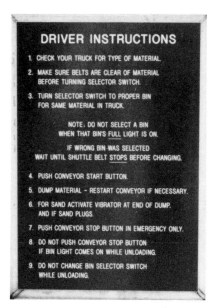

Even with a good transportation network in place, it is not economical to haul concrete long distances. Catalina Pacific Concrete operates thirteen batch plants in locations extending from Wilmington to Riverside.

Publications often have an "Acknowledgments" section devoted to recognition of those "without whose help this publication would not have been possible." Acknowledgments in this publication recognizes those who have helped make the California Portland Cement Company centennial possible.

Some have taken part in the executive and managerial decisions which have shaped the course of the company. Others have been involved in implementing those decisions at all levels. Some helped

Employees with 40 to 44 years of Service

WARREN C. ALLINGHAM	LARRY J. GEZELIUS, JR.	MANUAL T. LUNA
ROBERT BRAZEAU	ANASTACIO GONZALEZ	MILFORD LYNN
DEWEY BUSHONG	CARMEN GUERRERO	BILL MABERY
DANIEL CAMPA	TONY GUERRERO	RAYMOND MADSEN
ROMAN CAMPA	KERMIT HAYDEN	ROBERT MARTUS
RAFAEL CARLOS	DALE HENDRICKSON	CHARLES MAYER
MARTINIANO CARREON	EMIL HODGE	JAMES MCDOWELL
ARTURO CASTORENA	HARRY HOUGH	IGNACIO MENDOZA
PEDRO CHAVEZ	RALPH HUBBS	BASILIO MORALES
MANUEL CIMENTAL	ROSS HUBBS	NORRIS NORDENSTAM
TONY COLUNGA	WILLIAM JARRELL	ANTONIO PEREZ
FELIX CORTEZ	JESUS JUAREZ	CARLOS PEREZ
HOWARD DEWITT	THOMAS LATIMER	ROBERT PETERSON
SCHUYLER DONNEL	AMBROSIO LEON	SALVADOR PIMENTEL
CONCEPCION FIGUEROA	LEON LOOMIS	ARTHUR RAZO
ANDY GASCA	FRANCISCO LOPEZ	MANUEL RAZO
NORBERTO GASCA	ARTHUR LUNA	ALEJANDRO RODRIGUEZ

D G M E N T S

the company celebrate its Golden Anniversary.

Special recognition is given to those who, in the course of the company's first 100 years, spent four decades or more as a California Portland Cement Company employee. These are members of what has arbitrarily been called the Over Forty Club. There are no rules and regulations associated with the "club" and the only entrance requirement is based on length of service, but the membership is composed of very special people.

ANTONIO TORRES   PETE VARGAS   LESTER WILLIAMS

ANTONIO G. TORREZ   ISIDRO VILLALOBOS   OLIVER WILSON

FINIS TRUSTY   WILLIAM WATSON   WILLIAM ZENDEJAS

Employees With 45 to 49 Years of Service

CARMEN Z. CERVANTES   TONY LIZARDE   ROBERT G. PATTERSON

ESEQUIEL CHAVEZ   ELOY MARTINEZ   ROSCOE SCHOTT

ERNEST E. DUQUE   VERNON MONSON   CHARLES SMITH

ALFONZO LEYVA   FRANK OLSEN (GROSS)   FRANK THORNBERRY

Employees With 50 or More Years of Service

LEM E. BANCROFT   ARCHIE M. MCCALL

WILSON C. HANNA   BASILIO MARTINEZ

ERNIE I. HENDRICKSON

"We are all too busy working to work on our history," stated one of the History Committee members early in the development of this project. For that reason they welcomed someone who could devote full time to the project.

The History Committee members, however, were not too busy to provide invaluable assistance to the project. The centennial year was a particularly busy one for the company with significant decisions made in many areas which impacted the committee members.

This, however, did not prevent them from always being willing and able to provide information on how things were done and who had done them. It did not prevent them from generously and graciously giving of their time and sharing their knowledge and resources.

We are particularly indebted to Kermit Hayden for sharing his vast collection of memorabilia and serving as the unofficial historian, even in retirement. The publication would not have been possible without his assistance. Dale Hendrickson offered information on his family's long association with both the Mojave and the Colton plants. Jerry Jerrard went to great lengths to provide information on Catalina Pacific. He worked with Ann Morris in locating information about its ancestors.

Dave Cahn gave the centennial project direction through the initial suggestions for History Committee membership and guided it through the corporate offices. Gary Thornberry was always ready with research materials and family recollections about Colton and Rillito.

I suspect this would have been a much different publication if it had not been for Brent Loomis and his suggestion for an author — as well as his conscientious perusal of draft text and support in providing information on many of the past job titles used.

All the committee members were working at doing their jobs or at carrying on their personal lives, but they also took the time to work at discovering a bit more about the history of California Portland Cement Company and for that we owe them a vote of thanks.

Thanks also is extended to members of the California Portland Cement family both past and present who took the time to provide information, memorabilia or interviews.

A particular debt is owed Ian Smith for his excellent paper on *A History of Mining Operations at Mt. Slover Colton, California.* This provides intriguing detail on the mining which took place, as well as historical background on both the site and the man for whom it is named.

The authors of earlier company histories provided a solid basis for both information and graphics which found their way into the centennial publication. Frank Thornberry's paper on the history of the Rillito plant proved very helpful, as did the recollections of Fran Young and Fred Kennett. Fred also generously made available early photos of the Arizona Portland Cement plant.

Verb Holcomb provided taped interviews of employees. The interviews had been conducted by Ian

Smith. Michael Morphy, Ron Evans, Fred Kennett, Joana Pierce, Dale Hendrickson, and Kermit Hayden each spent several hours being interviewed specifically for the centennial publication.

Roscoe Schott was available on request for clarification of information about past employees with whom he had worked.

We are indebted to current employees who were not on the History Committee, but took the time to check copy for accuracy, look into their files, and provide information, articles and artifacts simply because they were interested in the centennial project.

Sharon DeHayes helped locate photographs of Colton and contributed to the section on Catalina Pacific. Bill Brack and Don Collins were also helpful in gathering information for this section. Background for the "Sites" section was provided by Leo Mercy, although its adaptation to the text was strictly the responsibility of the author, whose training in geology was minimal!

John Vidergar shared his file on the company's history and Jan Stevens took time to proof and comment upon drafts of the text. Peggy Land kept at least two members of the History Committee on track and was always able to locate them when the author had "immediate" questions to be answered.

It is always tempting to conclude recognition of those who have assisted with the comment that there are others "too numerous to mention," but while there are numerous others, they deserve mention. Assistance was provided by John Rains, Mardi Nagy, Tom Brosnan, Mike Robertson, Bob Brezsny, Schuyler Donnel.

Joe Cordero, Phillip Campa, Jackie Stoker and Ramon Corral provided genea-

logical information on people who were and are part of the cement plant "family."

There were others outside the family whose interest and work in history were most helpful. Hazel Olson's book *As The Sand Shifts In Colton, California* contained background material on both the company and the city for which its product is named. Jim Fox was kind enough to locate some historic photos of Colton for reproduction in this publication.

Finally, "Thanks" hardly seems adequate to express appreciation for the tolerance of the Wilson and Senn families who put up with long hours of focused activity which excluded them and interjected itself into what would have been a summer of normal activity. Their patience, support and understanding is deeply appreciated and we hope they will look back on the time spent on this publication with a sense that they also contributed.

Top: *Dale Hendrickson (left), Brent Loomis (right).*

Bottom: *left to right, Kermit Hayden, Gary Thornberry and Jerry Jarrard.*

Opposite: *left to right, Chuck Wilson, Sandy Bradley and Dave Cahn.*

INDEX

D

E

F

G

H

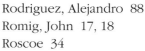

T

U

V

W

Y

Z

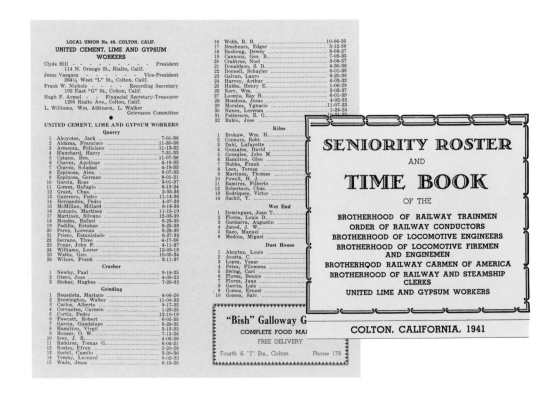